Progress in Mathematics

2 CORE

Les Murray BA

Senior Teacher and Head of Mathematics, Garstang County High School

Stanley Thornes (Publishers) Ltd

First published in 1985 by Stanley Thornes (Publishers) Ltd
Old Station Drive, Leckhampton, CHELTENHAM GL53 0DN, UK.

British Library Cataloguing in Publication Data

Murray, L.
  Progress in mathematics.
  Book 2C
  I. Title
  510   QA37.2

  ISBN 0-85950-180-9

To BAM and LM

Typeset by Grafikon Ltd, Oostkamp, Belgium.
Printed and bound in Great Britain at The Bath Press, Avon

Preface

As with the first-year books, I have written numerous, carefully graded questions, so once again the teacher must be selective. Few worked examples have been given thus allowing for alternative methods of introducing topics.

Revision work has been provided where necessary and a revision section has been inserted every six chapters, questions being based on those chapters.

Once again, photocopy masters are available to the teacher for exercises where pupils may benefit by their provision. Such exercises have been labelled **M**.

Total dependence on a calculator is not encouraged and the use of such is at the discretion of the teacher. In certain exercises I have recommended that a calculator should be used, while for some others I have suggested that one should not be used.

The completion of this book has been dependent on the valued help and advice given to me by many people, in particular by Mrs Alice Dickson of Garstang High School, who has carefully and painstakingly worked through the whole text and has provided the answers as well as giving welcome advice; and to Mr J. Britton, Head of Mathematics at Copthall School, London, for his most useful comments. My thanks also go to the staff and pupils of Garstang High School for their interest and co-operation while writing has been in progress.

I would also like to thank Mr M.J. Stewart of the Royal Lancaster Hospital and the Council of Royal Lytham and St. Annes Golf Club for supplying useful information.

Les Murray
1985

Contents

1 Sets

Here are some *closed curves*:

You can start anywhere on a closed curve and follow the line without breaking off at any point. You will arrive at the starting point again.

This is not a closed curve:

Here are some *simple closed curves*:

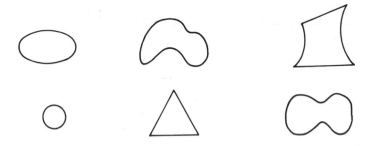

A simple closed curve does not cross over itself.

This closed curve ⟨⟩ is *not* a simple closed curve because it crosses over itself.

Exercise 1

Which of these are simple closed curves?

1.

6.

2.

7.

3.

8.

4.

9.

5.

Exercise 2

1. Draw 5 simple closed curves of your own.

2. Draw 5 curves that are not simple closed curves.

Exercise 3

Here is a *Venn diagram*.
It shows the set of counting
numbers between 8 and 15.

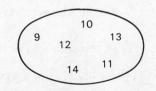

Show each of these sets on a Venn diagram:

1. The set of counting numbers less than 10

2. The set of even numbers less than 15

3. The set of numbers that are less than 42 and that divide exactly by 5

4. The set of colours used in traffic lights in this country

5. The set of months of the year that begin with the letter J

6. The set of counting numbers that lie between 20 and 35

7. The set of letters in the alphabet that follow the letter q

8. The set of British coins

9. The set of numbers that lie between 8 and 35 and that divide exactly by 3

10. The set of letters in the word PENCIL

11. The set of odd numbers that lie between 50 and 60

12. The set of multiples of 7 that are less than 30

Sets can be listed inside curly brackets.
Curly brackets look like this:

$$\{ \qquad\qquad\qquad \}$$

Exercise 4

A Practise drawing curly brackets.
Try to fit them between the lines on your page as follows:

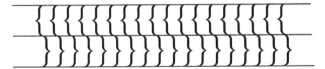

B The set of counting numbers between 8 and 15
  = {9, 10, 11, 12, 13, 14}.
Note the curly brackets. The set above has six *members*. The members of a set must be separated by commas.
List these sets. Use curly brackets and commas.

1. The set of odd numbers that are less than 12

2. The set of days of the week

3. The set of vowels

4. The set of suits in a pack of cards

5. The set of numbers less than 100 that divide exactly by 10

6. The set of months of the year that have seven letters

7. The set of items of cutlery

8. The set of letters in the word METRIC

9. The set of the first seven even numbers

10. The set of prime numbers less than 20

Exercise 5

Show these sets on Venn diagrams. (Use simple closed curves.)

1. A set of sports = {netball, cricket, hockey, football}

2. A set of boys' names = {Alan, Ben, Colin}

3. The set of divisors of 12 = {1, 2, 3, 4, 6, 12}

4. The set of letters of the alphabet following s
  = {t, u, v, w, x, y, z}

5. A set of fruit = {apple, banana, pear, orange, grape}

Exercise 6

Write these sets using curly brackets.
Members must be separated by commas.

1.

destroyer liner tug aircraft carrier

2.

8 40 48 64 56 16 24 72 32

3.

diamond ruby emerald sapphire pearl topaz

4.

k m n q p o l

5.

dog budgie goldfish cat rabbit

6.

gas oil coal electricity

Exercise 7

Here is a list of sets:

1. A set of capital cities

2. A set of footwear

3. A set of things to collect

4. The set of letters in the word TRIANGLE

5. A set of stringed instruments

6. A set of numbers that divide exactly by 4

7. A set of metric units of length

8. A set of colours

9. The set of counting numbers between 100 and 110

10. The set of planets

Here are the same sets listed in curly brackets.
The order is different.
Match these sets to those given above.

e.g.   A set of capital cities = {London, Paris, Amsterdam, Rome}

{A, E, G, I, L, N, R, T}

{violin, viola, cello, double bass}

{shoes, boots, slippers, clogs, trainers}

{101, 102, 103, 104, 105, 106, 107, 108, 109}

{London, Paris, Amsterdam, Rome}

{20, 12, 32, 208, 16, 28, 52, 64, 80}

{red, blue, green}

{Mercury, Venus, Earth, Mars, Jupiter, Saturn, Uranus, Neptune, Pluto}

{kilometre, hectometre, decametre, metre, decimetre, centimetre, millimetre}

{stamps, marbles, coins, key rings}

Exercise 8

Describe these sets in words:

1. {rose, pansy, daisy, tulip, snowdrop}

2. {onion, bean, turnip, carrot, leek}

3. {house, bungalow, cottage, flat, caravan}

4. {red, orange, yellow, green, blue, indigo, violet}

5. {ash, elm, oak, beech}

6. {square, rectangle, rhombus, parallelogram, kite, trapezium}

7. {equilateral triangle, isosceles triangle, right-angled triangle, scalene triangle}

8. {Spring, Summer, Autumn, Winter}

9. {62, 102, 142, 232, 612, 892, 952}

10. {Ann, Brenda, Carol, Dawn, Eileen}

Exercise 9

Copy each set and fill in the missing members:

1. Here is the set of odd numbers that are less than 20:

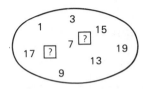

2. The set of letters in the word HOUSE = {E, H, O, ? , U}

3. The set of letters following m in the alphabet
   { ? , o, p, q, r, ? , t, u, v, ? , x, ? , z}

4. The set of numbers less than 80 that end in 7
   = {77, 37, 57, 7, 17, ? , 27, ? }

5. The set of even numbers less than 20
   = {6, ? , 2, ? , 4, 8, 12, 14, 18}

6. The set of suits in a pack of cards
   = {hearts, ? , diamonds, spades}

7. The set of multiples of 6 that lie between 10 and 50
   = {12, 18, ? , ? , 36, ? , 48}

8. The set of types of triangles
   = {scalene triangle, ? , ? , right-angled triangle}

9. The set of factors of 24
   = {1, ? , ? , 4, ? , 8, ? , 24}

7

Exercise 10

In each of these sets, one member is wrong. Write the odd one out.

1. {rose, tulip, daffodil, cauliflower, sunflower}
2. {horse, cow, pig, tiger, sheep}
3. {salt, fork, pepper, sauce, mustard}
4. {cup, glass, mug, kettle}
5. {car, bus, lorry, aeroplane, van}
6. {2, 4, 6, 8, 9, 10, 12}
7. {53, 43, 34, 73, 93, 103, 263}
8. {finger, eye, nose, mouth, ear}
9. {Nile, Amazon, Everest, Danube, Thames}
10. {six, octagon, ten, twelve, eighteen, twenty}

Exercise 11

Write the wrong member from each of these sets:

1. A set of fish = {haddock, trout, plaice, cod, whale}
2. A set of odd numbers = {11, 19, 261, 162, 345, 309}
3. A set of even numbers less than 10 = {2, 4, 6, 8, 10}
4. A set of numbers ending in 4 = {354, 423, 144, 764}
5. A set of birds = {ladybird, robin, sparrow, thrush}
6. A set of hats = {cap, tea cosy, trilby, stetson, turban}
7. A set of insects = {beetle, bee, wasp, aunt, fly}
8. A set of islands = {Greenland, Iceland, Italy, Great Britain}
9. A set of divisors of 24 = {1, 2, 3, 4, 6, 8, 9, 12, 24}
10. A set of solids = {hexagon, cone, sphere, cube, cuboid}

Exercise 12

1. Here is a set of numbers:
{3, 5, 6, 8, 10, 15, 50}
Write a set of numbers where the members are twice as big as the members of the set above.

2. Look at this set of numbers:
{6, 8, 18, 20, 40, 64}
Write a set of numbers where the members are half as big as the members of the set above.

3. Write a set of numbers where the members are 3 times as big as the members of the set:
{2, 5, 6, 7, 9, 10, 20, 25, 200}

4. Write a set of numbers where the members are 10 times as big as the members of the set:
{1, 2, 4, 5, 9, 10, 30, 52}

5. Write a set of numbers where the members are 10 more than the members of this set:
{6, 8, 14, 19, 23, 46, 95}

Exercise 13

1. From the given set, list:
   (*a*) The set of odd numbers
   (*b*) The set of even numbers
   (*c*) The set of numbers
       that divide exactly by 3

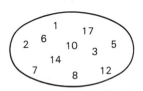

2. Here is a set of numbers:
{103, 123, 145, 253, 340, 415}
From the given set, list:
(*a*) The set of odd numbers
(*b*) The set of even numbers
(*c*) The set of numbers that divide exactly by 5

3. Here is a set of shapes:

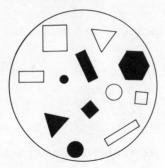

From the given set, using Venn diagrams, show:
(*a*) The set of squares
(*b*) The set of triangles
(*c*) The set of black shapes

4. Here is a set of liquids:
{water, petrol, paraffin, milk, lemonade}
From the given set, using a Venn diagram, show the set of drinks.

5. Here is a set of numbers:
{14, 20, 24, 30, 35, 51, 72, 99}
From the given set, list:
(*a*) The set of multiples of 5
(*b*) The set of multiples of 3

$\in$ means 'is a member of' (or 'belongs to')
$\notin$ means 'is not a member of' (or 'does not belong to')

We can write:
Lake Windermere $\in$ the set of lakes
River Mersey $\notin$ the set of lakes

The same sentences can be written like this:
Lake Windermere $\in$ {lakes}
River Mersey $\notin$ {lakes}

{lakes} is read as 'the set of lakes'
{rivers} is read as 'the set of rivers'

Exercise 14

Copy these. Replace each question mark with ∈ or ∉ to make each sentence true.

1. 7 ? {odd numbers}

2. 24 ? {odd numbers}

3. 18 ? {3, 6, 8, 10, 12, 13, 17, 18, 24, 26}

4. 28 ? {3, 6, 9, 12, 15 18, 21, 24, 27, 30, 33}

5. tennis racquet ? {sports equipment}

6. pen ? {things to write with}

7. red admiral ? {butterflies}

8. green ? {colours in the Union Jack}

9. copper ? {metals}

10. eggs ? {ingredients in a fruitcake}

Exercise 15

For each statement, write whether it is true or false:

1. 46 ∈ {even numbers}

2. carrot ∉ {fruit}

3. elm ∉ {trees}

4. I ∈ {letters in the word SQUARE}

5. pentagon ∉ {polygons}

6. necklace ∉ {jewellery}

7. chair ∉ {furniture}

8. 498 ∉ {numbers that end in 8}

9. 184 ∈ {numbers that lie between 100 and 160}

10. 275 ∉ {numbers that lie between 250 and 275}

An *empty set* is a set with no members.
It is written as $\varnothing$ or { }.

Exercise 16

Which of these are empty sets?
Write $\varnothing$ if a set is empty. If a set is not empty, write 'IS NOT AN EMPTY SET'.

1. The set of quadrilaterals with four sides

2. The set of even numbers ending in 4

3. {even numbers that divide exactly by 3}

4. {tins of spotted paint}

5. The set of adults under 15 years of age

6. {ice cubes above 10 °C}

7. {dates in January between 1st and 31st}

8. The set of cars with fewer than three wheels.

9. The set of odd numbers ending in 0

10. {empty bottles}

Exercise 17

How many members has each of these sets?

1. {red, green, yellow, blue, brown}

2. {7, 9, 10, 13, 15, 16, 18, 21, 23, 25, 26}

3. {days of the week on which you go to school}

4. The set of months in a year

5. {months of the year whose names begin with T}

6. The set of days in the month of May

7. The set of odd numbers between 8 and 18

8. The set of odd numbers between 108 and 118

9. {whole numbers between 14 and 19}

10. {whole numbers between 36 and 48}

11. {whole numbers between 43 and 97}

12. {whole numbers between 32 and 50 that divide exactly by 3}

13. The set of odd numbers less than 15

14. {whole numbers less than 5 that are bigger than 8}

15. The set of divisors of 12

Exercise 18

1. Find the sum of the set of numbers in:

   (a) The circle
   (b) The triangle
   (c) The square
   (d) The triangle only
   (e) The circle or the square or both but not in the triangle

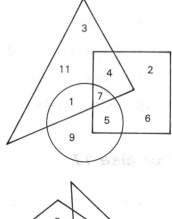

2. (a) Find the sum of the set of numbers in the triangle.
   (b) Find the total of the set of numbers in the pentagon.
   (c) Which number is in the rectangle only?

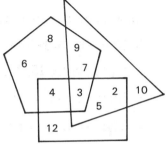

   (d) Find the difference between the largest number in the rectangle and the smallest number in the pentagon.

13

(e) Find the total of the numbers that are in the rectangle or the triangle or both but are not in the pentagon.

3. Copy the diagram.
Fill in the missing three numbers so that the triangle total = 25, the circle total = 32, and the rectangle total = 31.

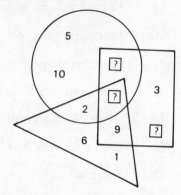

4. Draw another diagram as in question 3 using a circle, rectangle and triangle. Fill in the numbers as follows (put one number in each part of the diagram):
6 goes in the triangle only.
5 goes in the rectangle only.
7 goes in the triangle and circle but not the rectangle.
4 goes in all three shapes.
The triangle and rectangle each total 19.
The circle total = 28.

2 Number

Exercise 1

1. How many digits has each number?
   (a) 3265   (b) 506 312   (c) 7 649 158

2. Copy and complete:
   (a)   54 = ? tens   + ? units
   (b)   612 = ? hundreds + ? ten   + ? units
   (c) 8379 = ? thousands + ? hundreds + ? tens
       + ? units

3. Write in figures in the normal way:
   (a) 4 tens and 8 units
   (b) 3 hundreds + 9 tens + 7 units
   (c) 5 hundreds + 0 tens + 1 unit
   (d) 9 thousands + 2 hundreds + 6 tens + 3 units

4. (a) 700 + 20 + 5 = ?
   (b) 9000 + 300 + 60 + 1 = ?

5. (a) 90 + 600 + 3 = ?
   (b) 2000 + 7 + 400 + 10 = ?
   (c) 500 + 30 + 8000 = ?

6. (a) seven + eight hundred + twenty = ?
   (b) nine + three hundred = ?
   (c) 40 + five thousand + sixty + 100 = ?

7. (a)   82 + 10   (d)   60 + 421
   (b)   56 + 20   (e)   503 + 80
   (c) 700 + 247   (f)   465 + 400

8. (a) Write two hundred and forty-five in figures.

(b) Write six thousand, one hundred and seven in figures.

(c) Write five thousand, nine hundred and twenty-four in figures.

9. Write in words:

(a) 359   (b) 4736   (c) 2861

10. (a) List the even numbers that lie between 25 and 45.

(b) List the odd numbers that are greater than 60 but less than 75.

Exercise 2

1. Write these numbers in order. Put the largest first.

(a) 15, 94, 7, 126, 140, 22, 91, 109

(b) 3062, 497, 7123, 5602, 3206, 749, 479

2. Write the smallest number from each set:

(a) 63, 71, 84, 49, 409, 37, 48, 39 or 102

(b) 3826, 3628, 3268, 3286, 3682 or 3862

(c) 5207, 5270, 5072, 5027, 5702 or 5720

(d) 9162, 8999, 8099, 9612, 9354 or 9081

3. Copy these, and fill in the correct sign, < or > :

(a) 6103 ? 2849   (b) 5021 ? 5102

4. Using any of the digits 3, 5, 6 and 9 once only in each number, write:

(a) the smallest 4-digit number that can be made,

(b) the largest 3-digit number that can be made,

(c) the largest even number that can be made.

Exercise 3

Carry out these calculations:

1.	**2.**	**3.**	**4.**
52	603	7125	368
+ 37	+ 174	+ 1630	10
			+ 7521

5.	46	**7.**	567	**9.**	5613	**11.**	6289
	+ 18		+ 214		+ 2768		+ 2354

6.	284	**8.**	3086	**10.**	1642	**12.**	3612
	+ 370		+ 1409		+ 5439		507
							28
							+ 1434

13. 64 + 25   **20.** 12 + 187 + 77
14. 38 + 641   **21.** 3169 + 203 + 31
15. 192 + 463   **22.** 574 + 17 + 8166
16. 726 + 49   **23.** 4008 + 470 + 1032
17. 2305 + 516   **24.** 19 + 613 + 2814
18. 406 + 2137   **25.** 2107 + 8 + 26 + 335
19. 149 + 326 + 274

Exercise 4

1. Add 100 to each of these numbers:
   (a) 281   (b) 926   (c) 3605   (d) 74

2. Add 39 to each of these numbers:
   (a) 50   (b) 240   (c) 621   (d) 428

3. Copy and complete the magic square:

		12
		13
	15	8

4. Find the sum of 48 and 32.

5. My marks in four tests were 67, 45, 71, and 58. Find my total mark.

17

6. Copy and complete the mapping:

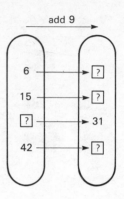

7. Copy and complete:

12, 17 $\xrightarrow{\quad + \quad}$?

8. Find the value of:
   (a) 7 + 9 + 3   (b) 42 + 67 + 58

9. (a) Is 57 closer to 50 or to 60?
   (b) Is 645 closer to 600 or to 700?
   (c) Is 2613 closer to 2000 or to 3000?

10. (a) Round 78 to the nearest ten.
   (b) Round 452 to the nearest hundred.
   (c) Round 6301 to the nearest thousand.

11. Estimate the answers to these:
   (a) 63 + 86 + 59   (b) 567 + 224 + 483

12. Copy these and fill in the missing digits:

(a)
```
    3 ? 6
  + 1 5 ?
  ───────
  ? 0 3
```

(b)
```
    2 5 ? ?
  + 4 ? 6 8
  ─────────
  ? 5 2 2
```

(c)
```
    7 2 5 4
  + ? ? ? ?
  ─────────
  9 2 3 6
```

Exercise 5

Use a calculator to help you with these:

A
1. 706 + 285
2. 1253 + 694
3. 961 + 84 + 167
4. 7832 + 9 + 543

5. 24 + 331 + 69
6. 2870 + 5447
7. 6139 + 996
8. 217 + 1374 + 845

9. 76 + 67 + 303
10. 7014 + 298 + 916

B Write which statements are true and which are false:

1. $64 + 57 = 57 + 64$
2. $72 + 27 = 100$
3. $327 + 463 = 723 - 364$
4. $506 + 208 = 714$
5. $395 + 647 = 1142$
6. $915 + 258 = 1173$
7. $813 + 318 = 1131$
8. $602 + 398 = 398 + 602$
9. $280 + 635 = 635 + 280$
10. $4316 + 2507 = 2507 + 4316$

Exercise 6

1.
$$\begin{array}{r} 85 \\ -23 \\ \hline \end{array}$$

4.
$$\begin{array}{r} 524 \\ -271 \\ \hline \end{array}$$

7.
$$\begin{array}{r} 900 \\ -468 \\ \hline \end{array}$$

9.
$$\begin{array}{r} 3178 \\ -916 \\ \hline \end{array}$$

2.
$$\begin{array}{r} 713 \\ -302 \\ \hline \end{array}$$

5.
$$\begin{array}{r} 862 \\ -433 \\ \hline \end{array}$$

8.
$$\begin{array}{r} 713 \\ -285 \\ \hline \end{array}$$

10.
$$\begin{array}{r} 6721 \\ -2063 \\ \hline \end{array}$$

3.
$$\begin{array}{r} 34 \\ -19 \\ \hline \end{array}$$

6.
$$\begin{array}{r} 602 \\ -156 \\ \hline \end{array}$$

11. $69 - 27$
12. $761 - 216$
13. $1636 - 922$
14. $5482 - 2756$
15. $4907 - 1482$
16. $7815 - 2368$
17. $6074 - 4887$
18. $4001 - 1672$
19. $9238 - 6145$
20. $8563 - 4076$

Exercise 7

A Copy these and fill in the missing numbers:

1. $15 - \boxed{?} = 9$
2. $32 - \boxed{?} = 13$
3. $\boxed{?} - 21 = 38$
4. $100 - \boxed{?} = 64$
5. $\boxed{?} - 59 = 100$

B Copy each question and fill in the missing digits:

1. 5 6
   − ?2 2
   ‾‾‾‾‾
     2 ?

2. 3 ?7 7
   − 1 5 ?
   ‾‾‾‾‾‾‾
   ?3 3

3. ?1 1 ?
   − 5 2 8
   ‾‾‾‾‾‾‾
     2 ?8 8

4. 8 2 3
   − ?? ?? ??
   ‾‾‾‾‾‾‾
     4 7 6

C **1.** Subtract 10 from 382.

2. Take 10 from 97.

3. Take 10 from 206.

4. Subtract 100 from 631.

5. Take 100 from 3192.

D Copy and complete these mapping diagrams:

1.

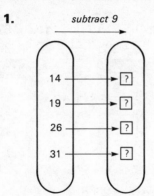

subtract 9

2.

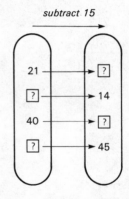

subtract 15

E **1.** How much change would you get out of £1 if you spent 72 p?

2. What must I add to 43 to make 100?

3. Take 36 from 86.

4. From 71 take 25.

5. If 39 + ?? = 100, find the missing number.

6. What number, when subtracted from 53 gives 29?

7. What number, when added to 47 gives 95?

8. The difference between two numbers is 18. If the larger number is 40, find the smaller number.

20

Exercise 8

This nomogram can be used for addition.

You need to use a ruler.

Try to see how it works.

Use the nomogram to find the answers to these questions:

1. $8 + 12$
2. $16 + 10$
3. $20 + 20$
4. $4 + 14$
5. $21 + 19$
6. $13 + 23$
7. $7 + 17$
8. $15 + 20$
9. $6 + 13$
10. $22 + 18$

23	46	23
22	44	22
21	42	21
20	40	20
19	38	19
18	36	18
17	34	17
16	32	16
15	30	15
14	28	14
13	26	13
12	24	12
11	22	11
10	20	10
9	18	9
8	16	8
7	14	7
6	12	6
5	10	5
4	8	4
3	6	3
2	4	2
1	2	1
0	0	0

Exercise 9

The nomogram can also be used for subtraction.
Try to see how it works.

Use the nomogram to find the answers to these:

1. $22 - 8$
2. $34 - 14$
3. $26 - 5$
4. $46 - 23$
5. $14 - 6$
6. $30 - 11$
7. $24 - 16$
8. $28 - 6$
9. $36 - 15$
10. $18 - 7$
11. $25 - 19$
12. $15 - 6$
13. $33 - 23$
14. $36 - 20$
15. $37 - 20$

21

Exercise 10

1. Copy this rectangle and fill in the numbers:

4	7	10	13	16	19	22	25		31
9	12				24				
14	17								
19			31						46
24									51

2. Now write numbers in the empty squares by following these rules:

(*a*) Add 3 when you move one square to the right.

(*b*) Add 5 when you move one square downwards.

e.g. Start at 4 and move right $4 + 3 = \underline{7}$, $7 + 3 = \underline{10}$, and so on. Moving downwards, $4 + 5 = \underline{\underline{9}}$, $9 + 5 = \underline{\underline{14}}$, and so on. Note that 24 is written under 19 since $19 + 5 = \underline{\underline{24}}$.

Exercise 11

1. (*a*) Alan found 7 conkers, then 5 more. He gave 3 to Christine. How many did he keep?

    (*b*) Carol had 2056 stamps and was given 825 more. She gave 562 to Peter. How many did she keep?

2. (*a*) James had 12 marbles. He lost 4 and was given 7 more. How many did he then have?

    (*b*) Felicia had 391 cards. She lost 127 and was given 164 more. How many did she then have?

3. (*a*) Mary ate 3 cakes. Claire ate twice as many and 4 more. How many did Claire eat?

    (*b*) Dave delivered 128 newspapers. Bill delivered twice as many and 67 more. How many did Bill deliver?

4. (*a*) Kate had 11 biscuits. She ate 3 then gave half of what was left to Ron. How many biscuits did Kate have left?

(*b*) June had 86 sweets. She ate 14 then gave half of what was left to Ken. How many sweets did June have left?

Darts

A dartboard is divided into sectors.

The scores for each sector are given as numbers on the dartboard.

In the centre of a dartboard is the bull's eye. The score in the bull's eye is fifty.

Around the bull's eye is a 'ring'. The score in that ring is 25.

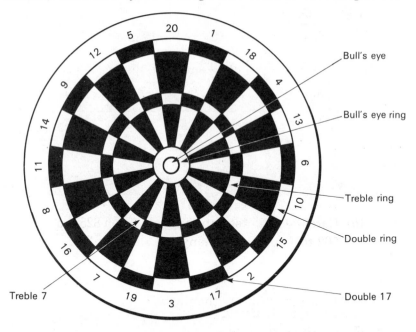

There are two more rings. The outer ring near the numbers scores a double. If a dart lands in the 17 sector in the outer ring it scores double 17 (that is, 34). The other ring on a dartboard lies between the outer ring and the ring around the bull's eye. That ring is the treble. A dart that lands in the 7 sector in the treble ring scores treble 7 (that is, 21).

Copy and complete the table:

	Score from			Total
	First dart	Second dart	Third dart	
1.	14	6	8	
2.	20	1	5	
3.	20	20	14	
4.	double 4	10	6	
5.	double 6	13	13	
6.	8	double 8	11	
7.	double 15	2	double 10	
8.	17	double 2	double 3	
9.	treble 4	13	4	
10.	double 5	treble 5	20	

Exercise 13 ▬▬▬▬▬▬▬▬▬▬▬▬▬▬

A Write in figures:
1. 42 thousand
2. 67 thousand
3. 16 thousand
4. Twenty-eight thousand
5. Seventy-one thousand
6. Eighty-three thousand
7. Fourteen thousand
8. 90 thousand

B Write in words:

1. 54 000
2. 35 000
3. 29 000
4. 81 000
5. 76 000
6. 92 000
7. 17 000
8. 60 000

Exercise 14

Answer these:

1. (*a*)

$$\begin{array}{r} 21 \\ +36 \\ \hline \end{array}$$

(*b*)

$$\begin{array}{r} 21\,000 \\ +36\,000 \\ \hline \end{array}$$

2. (*a*)

$$\begin{array}{r} 45 \\ +28 \\ \hline \end{array}$$

(*b*)

$$\begin{array}{r} 45\,000 \\ +28\,000 \\ \hline \end{array}$$

3. (*a*)

$$\begin{array}{r} 74 \\ +19 \\ \hline \end{array}$$

(*b*)

$$\begin{array}{r} 74\,000 \\ +19\,000 \\ \hline \end{array}$$

4. (*a*) 32 + 46
(*b*) 32 000 + 46 000

5. (*a*) 33 + 29
(*b*) 33 000 + 29 000

6. (*a*) 40 + 46
(*b*) 40 000 + 46 000

7. (*a*) 14 + 35
(*b*) 14 000 + 35 000

8. (*a*) 26 + 64
(*b*) Twenty-six thousand + sixty-four thousand

Exercise 15

Answer these using a calculator:

A

1. 492 + 384
2. 861 − 295
3. 2034 − 1867
4. 3409 + 4063
5. 6213 − 3961
6. 4553 + 3554
7. 82 000 + 14 000
8. 76 000 − 38 000
9. 29 350 + 60 405
10. 38 049 + 15 687

B 1. Does 8361 − 3592 = 4869?
   2. Does 7216 + 2384 = 2384 + 7216?
   3. Does 6250 − 3967 = 3967 − 6250?
   4. Is 7179 + 8342 > 15 523?
   5. Is 12 361 − 7498 < 4873?

Exercise 16

Use a calculator for these:

A Use only the keys: $\boxed{2}\ \boxed{5}\ \boxed{+}\ \boxed{=}$

Try to obtain the given numbers on the display.

e.g. $\boxed{5} + \boxed{5} + \boxed{5} + \boxed{2} + \boxed{2} = 19$

1. 9	**3.** 24	**5.** 6
2. 14	**4.** 17	

B Use only the keys: $\boxed{6}\ \boxed{7}\ \boxed{+}\ \boxed{=}$

Try to obtain these numbers on the display.

1. 19	**3.** 12	**5.** 17
2. 20	**4.** 25	

C Use only the keys: $\boxed{5}\ \boxed{8}\ \boxed{+}\ \boxed{-}\ \boxed{=}$

Try to obtain:

1. 3	**3.** 19	**5.** 14
2. 11	**4.** 7	

D Use only the keys: $\boxed{4}\ \boxed{9}\ \boxed{+}\ \boxed{-}\ \boxed{=}$

Try to obtain:

1. 17	**3.** 23	**5.** 11
2. 14	**4.** 3	

Exercise 17

e.g. Write a 3-digit number.   723
      Reverse the digits.   327

Subtract the smaller number from the larger number.

$$\begin{array}{r} 723 \\ -\ 327 \\ \hline 396 \end{array}$$

Reverse the digits of your answer.   693

Add the last two numbers.

$$\begin{array}{r} 693 \\ +\ 396 \\ \hline 1089 \end{array}$$

1. Repeat the above steps for these numbers:
(*a*) 612   (*b*) 846   (*c*) 921   (*d*) 503   (*e*) 715
(*f*) What do you notice about all your answers?

2. (*a*) Make up four more examples.
      Use numbers you have thought of yourself.
(*b*) Try to find a 3-digit number that does not work.

Exercise 18

A Answer these:

1. $\begin{array}{r} 23 \\ \times\ 2 \\ \hline \end{array}$	**3.** $\begin{array}{r} 214 \\ \times\ 4 \\ \hline \end{array}$	**5.** $\begin{array}{r} 157 \\ \times\ 9 \\ \hline \end{array}$
2. $\begin{array}{r} 60 \\ \times\ 7 \\ \hline \end{array}$	**4.** $\begin{array}{r} 302 \\ \times\ 8 \\ \hline \end{array}$	

6. 3×56 **8.** $2 \times 5 \times 9$ **10.** $4 \times \boxed{?} = 8 \times 4$

7. 654×5 **9.** $5 \times 7 \times 4$

B Answer these:

1.

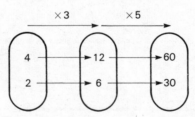

2.

3. Find the product of 6 and 34.

4. My car travels 47 miles on each gallon of petrol. How far does it travel on 8 gallons?

5. There are 56 gummed labels on a sheet. If I have 7 sheets of labels, how many labels have I altogether?

Exercise 19   **M**

Copy and complete these mappings:

e.g.

1. (*a*)

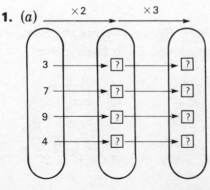

(*b*)

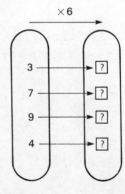

2. (a)

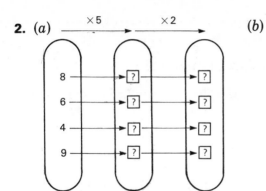

(b)

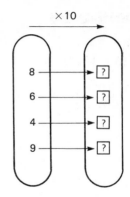

3.

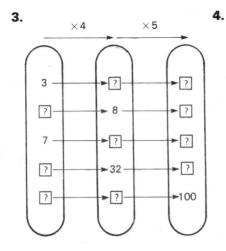

4.

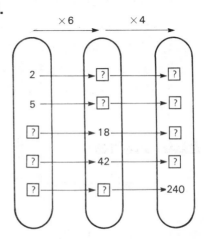

Exercise 20

Use a calculator to answer these. Before you use the calculator, try to say how many zeros there will be in the answer:

1. 30×40

2. 70×20

3. 4×8000

4. 900×50

5. 6000×70

6. 200×400

7. 8×3000

8. 90×2000

9. 600×8000

10. 7000×400

11. 300×500

12. 2000×6000

13. $80\,000 \times 9$

14. $30 \times 60\,000$

15. 4000×90

Exercise 21

Find the answers to these multiplications:

A 1. 10×5 4. 67×10 7. 704×10
   2. 10×50 5. 10×328 8. 10×390
   3. 10×500 6. 580×10

B 1. 5×100 4. 40×100 7. 100×250
   2. 100×35 5. 400×100 8. 4612×100
   3. 100×79 6. 195×100

C 1. 5×1000 4. 10×807 7. 1000×90
   2. 100×43 5. 285×1000 8. 100×90
   3. 1000×25 6. 390×1000

D 1. 3×20 4. 90×30 7. 40×80
   2. 70×2 5. 90×3 8. 40×71
   3. 9×30 6. 30×50

E 1. 4×200 4. 40×300 7. 300×23
   2. 700×5 5. 600×700 8. 84×6000
   3. 3000×5 6. 4000×40

Exercise 22

1. Round 4754 correct to the nearest thousand.
2. Round 6189 correct to the nearest thousand.
3. Round 840 correct to the nearest hundred.
4. Round 291 correct to the nearest hundred.
5. Round 209 correct to the nearest hundred.
6. Round 78 correct to the nearest ten.
7. Round 326 correct to the nearest hundred.

8. Round 47 correct to the nearest ten.

9. Round 52 correct to the nearest ten.

10. Round 735 correct to the nearest hundred.

11. Round 3698 correct to the nearest thousand.

12. Round 649 correct to the nearest hundred.

Exercise 23

e.g. 1 870×316
$\approx 900 \times 300$
$= \underline{270\,000}$

e.g. 2 6293×76
$\approx 6000 \times 80$
$= \underline{480\,000}$

Estimate the answer to these:

1. 42×69

2. 483×86

3. 308×726

4. 634×77

5. 196×780

6. 52×2164

7. 590×682

8. 5312×46

Exercise 24

A Copy and complete:

1.
```
      2 6
    × 2 3
    ─────
    5 2 0      20 × 26
  + [?][?]     3 × 26
    ─────
  [?] 9 [?]
```

3.
```
        4 9
    ×   2 5
    ───────
    [?] 8 0      20 × 49
  + [?][?] 5     5 × 49
    ───────
  [?][?][?] 5
```

2.
```
      5 7
    × 1 4
    ─────
    5 7 0      10 × 57
  +[?] 2 [?]    4 × 57
    ─────
  [?][?][?]
```

4.
```
        6 8
    ×   3 6
    ───────
  [?] 0 4 [?]    30 × 68
  + [?][?] 8     6 × 68
    ───────
  2 [?][?] 8
```

31

B Answer these. Set out your work as in part A:

  1. 43 × 32   **3.** 84 × 17   **5.** 41 × 64
  2. 97 × 35   **4.** 26 × 75   **6.** 59 × 82

Exercise 25

A Are these true or false? (Check them on a calculator.)

  1. 7 × 34 = 34 × 7   **6.** 3715 × 9 = 9 × 3715
  2. 61 × 93 = 93 × 61   **7.** 8247 × 6 = 8246 × 7
  3. 714 × 86 = 86 × 714   **8.** 790 × 21 = 79 × 210
  4. 47 × 28 = 74 × 82   **9.** 3480 × 300 = 348 000 × 3
  5. 98 × 102 = 89 × 201   **10.** 18 × 26 = 9 × 52

B Work these out on a calculator:

  1. If light travels 299 792 km in a second, how far does it travel in 12 s?

  2. 16 coaches each carry 49 passengers. How many people is that altogether?

  3. A shop sold 18 gross (a gross = 144) of pencils. How many was that?

  4. An astronaut follows an orbit of 28 170 km. How far is 56 of these orbits?

Exercise 26

A **1.** 4 girls share 24 sweets. How many does each get?

  2. 152 screws are put into packs of 8. How many packs are there?

  3. Copy and complete:

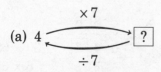
(a)

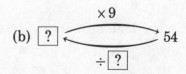
(b)

  4. A box contains 56 nails. How many times can I take 4 nails out of the box?

32

B Carry out these divisions:

1. $64 \div 2$

2. $3\overline{)78}$

3. $4\overline{)892}$

4. $6\overline{)456}$

5. $\dfrac{711}{9}$

6. $5\overline{)3275}$

7. $7\overline{)1302}$

8. $3\overline{)8106}$

9. $8672 \div 8$

10. $4\overline{)7132}$

11. $\dfrac{1340}{5}$

12. $\dfrac{7014}{6}$

13. $7\overline{)4354}$

14. $2\overline{)5718}$

15. $9\overline{)1926}$

C 1. 153 stamps are put into packs of 6. How many stamps are left over?

2. 264 pens are packed in boxes of 10. How many boxes do I need? How many pens are left over?

3. 348 marbles are shared equally by 9 boys.
How many does each boy get?
How many are left over?

Exercise 27

Estimate the answers to these:

1. $793 - 289$
2. $465 + 837$
3. $627 + 855 + 739$
4. 8×693
5. 924×7

6. $823 \div 4$
7. 6×478
8. $591 \div 3$
9. $542 + 916 + 283 + 664$
10. $807 + 775 + 142 + 369$

Exercise 28

Copy these. Put in the missing signs.
Choose from $+$, $-$, $\times$ or $\div$.

1. $24\ \boxed{?}\ 2 = 12$

2. $4\ \boxed{?}\ 6 = 10$

3. $8\ \boxed{?}\ 2\ \boxed{?}\ 4 = 4$

4. $6\ \boxed{?}\ 3\ \boxed{?}\ 5 = 13$

5. $12\ \boxed{?}\ 4\ \boxed{?}\ 3 = 6$

6. $2\ \boxed{?}\ 8 = 13\ \boxed{?}\ 3$

7. $4\ \boxed{?}\ 6 = 12\ \boxed{?}\ 12$

8. $30\ \boxed{?}\ 5 = 18\ \boxed{?}\ 12$

9. $10\ \boxed{?}\ 2 = 4\ \boxed{?}\ 3$

10. $12\ \boxed{?}\ 6 = 12\ \boxed{?}\ 2$

Exercise 29

Copy each of these. State whether it is true or false:

1. $7 \times 3\ < 13 + 9$

2. $2 \times 9\ < 12 + 6$

3. $4 + 12 =\ 8 \times 2$

4. $36 \div 4 > 12 - 3$

5. $6 \times 6 > 56 - 26$

6. $100 \div 4 <\ 5 \times 5$

Exercise 30

1. Tim was given 29 marbles. Jane was given 4 times as many. How many was Jane given?

2. How many seconds are there in 9 min?

3. 6 people shared 414 stamps equally among themselves. How many did each get?

4. 5 people shared 387 cards equally among themselves. How many cards were left?

5. Don and Linus shared 48 sweets so that Don got 6 more than Linus. How many did each get?

6. Pam and Paula shared 48 sweets equally. If Pam then gave Paula 6 of her sweets, how many did each then have?

34

Divisibility

Exercise 31

1. Copy this number line:

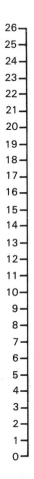

Mark on your number line, using dots, all the odd numbers as far as 25.

2. Make another number line.
Use dots on your new number line to show all the numbers that are divisible by 3.

Copy and complete this table:

9-times table	Sum of the digits
$2 \times 9 = 18$	$1 + 8 = 9$
$3 \times 9 = 27$	$2 + 7 = \boxed{?}$
$4 \times 9 = \boxed{?}$	$\boxed{?} + \boxed{?} = \boxed{?}$
$5 \times 9 = \boxed{?}$	$\boxed{?} + \boxed{?} = \boxed{?}$
$6 \times 9 = 54$	$5 + 4 = \boxed{?}$
$7 \times 9 = \boxed{?}$	$\boxed{?} + \boxed{?} = \boxed{?}$
$8 \times 9 = \boxed{?}$	$\boxed{?} + \boxed{?} = \boxed{?}$
$9 \times 9 = \boxed{?}$	$\boxed{?} + \boxed{?} = \boxed{?}$
$10 \times 9 = 90$	$9 + 0 = \boxed{?}$

What do you notice about the sum of the digits?

Exercise 33

A *e.g.* 135 divides exactly by 9.

Also, $1 + 3 + 5 = 9$. (The sum of the digits is 9.)

All the following numbers divide exactly by 9.

Check each one by dividing by 9.

Find the sum of the digits as in the example:

1. 126
2. 153
3. 180
4. 234
5. 306
6. 414
7. 432
8. 504

9. 531
10. 711
11. 1224
12. 1341
13. 2025
14. 2133
15. 4203

B What do you notice about the sum of the digits of numbers that divide exactly by 9?

Exercise 34

Which of these numbers divide exactly by 9?

1. 144
2. 163
3. 171
4. 190
5. 231
6. 360
7. 441
8. 512

9. 522
10. 621
11. 1053
12. 1402
13. 2115
14. 3042
15. 4121

Exercise 35

Here is a set of numbers:
{14, 15, 20, 24, 27, 54, 60, 75, 90, 135, 140, 375, 504, 980}

1. Which of the numbers divide exactly by 10?
2. Which of the numbers divide exactly by 2?
3. Which of the numbers divide exactly by 5?
4. Which of the numbers divide exactly by 9?

Number Patterns

Exercise 36

Copy these and give the next three steps:

1. 1 = 1
2 = 1 + 1
3 = 1 + 1 + 1
4 = 1 + 1 + 1 + 1
and so on

5. 2 × 9 = 18
22 × 9 = 198
222 × 9 = 1998
2222 × 9 = 19998
and so on

2. 1 = 1
11 = 10 + 1
111 = 100 + 10 + 1
1111 = 1000 + 100 + 10 + 1
and so on

6. 0 × 9 × 1 = 1
1 × 9 + 2 = 11
12 × 9 + 3 = 111
123 × 9 + 4 = 1111
and so on

3. 1 + 1 = 2
2 + 2 = 4
3 + 3 = 6
4 + 4 = 8
and so on

7. 0 × 2 + 1 = 1
1 × 3 + 1 = 4
2 × 4 + 1 = 9
3 × 5 + 1 = 16
and so on

4. 1 × 9 = 10 − 1
2 × 9 = 20 − 2
3 × 9 = 30 − 3
4 × 9 = 40 − 4
and so on

8. 1 × 1 = 1
11 × 11 = 121
111 × 111 = 12 321
and so on

3 Symbol — **Symmetry**

Bilateral Symmetry

Exercise 1

Which of these shapes are symmetrical?

1.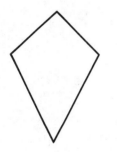

2.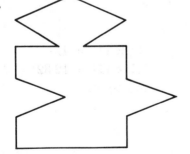

3.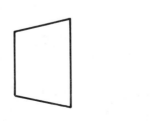

4.

5.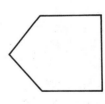

6.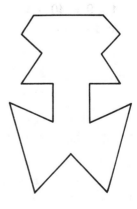

7.

8.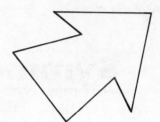

Exercise 2

The pattern shown in fig. 1 was obtained by folding a piece of paper then folding it a second time (fig. 2).

Pieces were then cut from the folded piece of paper to give the final shape.

Make your own symmetrical pattern in this way.
(Note that the pattern has two axes of symmetry.)

Fig. 1

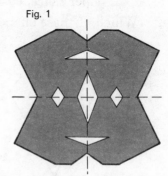

Fig. 2

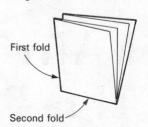

First fold

Second fold

Exercise 3

For each of these problems, fold a piece of paper twice. By cutting then unfolding, try to make:

1. a rectangle,
2. a square (use 2 straight cuts),
3. a square (use only 1 straight cut).

Exercise 4

1. Some letters of the alphabet can be made by folding
a piece of paper *once*, cutting out then unfolding
again.
Which letters of the alphabet can be made in this
way?

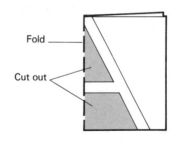

2. Which letters of the alphabet can be made by folding a piece
of paper *twice*, cutting out then unfolding again?

Exercise 5 M

Copy the following on to a sheet of paper. Complete each letter
so that the broken lines are axes of symmetry.

N ATHE MATICS IS
THE PEST S JPJECT
IN THE SCHOOL.
NOV VRITE YOUR
CVN SENTENCE

Copy these. Where possible, draw the axis (or axes) of symmetry for each shape. Some shapes have one axis, some have more than one, some have none.

1.

4.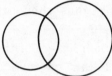

2.

5.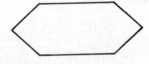

3.

6.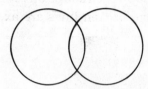

Exercise 7

For each shape, write the number of axes of symmetry:

1.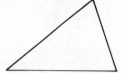

3.

2.

4.

5.

6.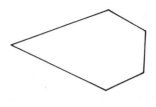

Exercise 8

Copy each shape on to squared paper. Complete each one so that
the broken lines are axes of symmetry.

Exercise 9

Copy these shapes. Complete each one so that the broken lines are axes of symmetry.

1.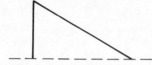

3.

2.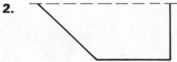

Exercise 10

Copy and complete.
Your finished pattern should have two axes of symmetry.

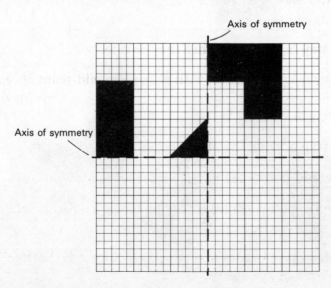

Exercise 11

1. Draw a rectangle 12 cm by 6 cm. (Use a set square.)

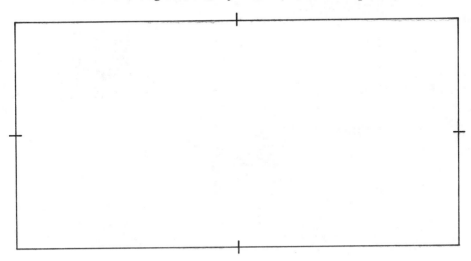

2. Mark the mid-point of each side.

3. Use a pair of compasses. With centre the mid-point of one of the shorter sides and radius 3 cm, draw a semi-circle inside the rectangle.

4. Repeat step 3 using the other shorter side.

5. Using a pair of compasses, with centre the mid-point of one of the longer sides and radius 6 cm, draw a semi-circle inside the rectangle.

6. Repeat step 5 using the other longer side.

7. Join the mid-points of opposite sides using straight lines.

8. With centre at the centre of the rectangle and with radius 3 cm, draw a circle.

9. The pattern has two axes of symmetry. Colour it so that it still has two axes of symmetry.

Use a mirror on this shape to make all the given shapes:

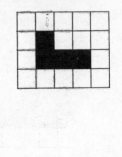

e.g. Question 1

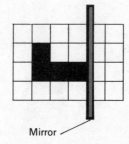

Mirror

Note: The mirror need not be at the edge of the shape.

Copy each shape on to squared paper:

1.

4.

2.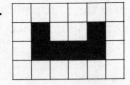

5.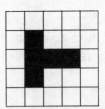

3.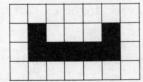

6.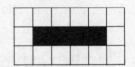

7.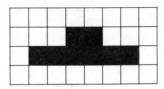

10.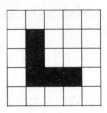

8.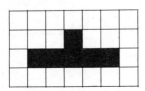

11.

9.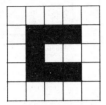

12.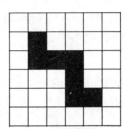

Exercise 13

Use a mirror on the given shape as in Exercise 12.

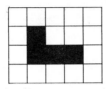

Make as many shapes of your own as you can.

Draw your answers on squared paper.

Rotational Symmetry

Exercise 14   To Make a Windmill

1. Cut out a square from a piece of paper (about 15 cm square).

   Fig. 1

2. Draw the two diagonals.

3. Cut along the diagonals from each vertex. Stop when you are about 15 mm from the centre of the square (fig. 1).

   Fig. 2

4. Put pin-pricks through the paper as shown in fig. 1.

5. Fold the four parts as shown in fig. 2 and fig. 3 but DO NOT CREASE.
   These are the windmill's sails.

   Fig. 3

6. Pin, or nail the sails to a stick. If you put a small bead between the stick and the sails, the sails will turn more easily.

The windmill's sails have *rotational symmetry*. A shape has rotational symmetry if it can be rotated to a new position to fit exactly on top of itself.

Exercise 15

Write 'YES' if a shape has rotational symmetry, otherwise write 'NO'. (You need not draw the shapes.)

1.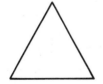

2.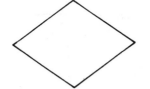

3.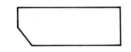

4.

5.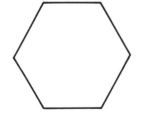

6.

7.

8.

9.

10.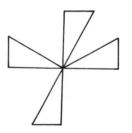

4 Fractions

A Copy the shapes and shade as instructed:

1. Shade $\frac{1}{2}$: (a)   (b)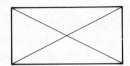

2. Shade $\frac{3}{4}$: (a)   (b)

B What fraction is:

1.

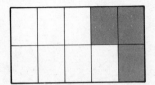

2.

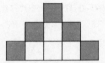

(a) shaded? (a) shaded?
(b) unshaded? (b) unshaded?

3.

4.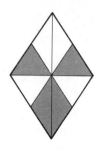

(a) shaded?

(b) unshaded?

(a) shaded?

(b) unshaded?

Exercise 2

1. Copy and complete:

   (a) ⬚ halves make a whole.

   (b) ⬚ ninths make a whole.

   (c) ⬚ tenths make a whole.

   (d) ⬚ sixteenths make a whole.

   (e) ⬚ hundredths make a whole.

2. Write in figures:

   (a) one-quarter   (b) three-eighths

3. Write in words:

   (a) $\dfrac{4}{5}$ (b) $\dfrac{7}{10}$

4. Write the numerator of these fractions:

   (a) $\dfrac{5}{8}$ (b) $\dfrac{13}{16}$

5. Write the denominator of these fractions:

   (a) $\dfrac{3}{4}$ (b) $\dfrac{15}{32}$

6. Draw a straight line:
   (*a*) 100 mm long. Divide it into tenths.
   (*b*) 80 mm long. Divide it into quarters.
   (*c*) 90 mm long. Divide it into sixths.

7. (*a*) A cake is cut into eighths.
        How many people can have one piece each?
   (*b*) Sweets are shared equally among 4 people.
        What fraction does each person get?
   (*c*) Tom spent one-half of his 70 p.
        How much did he spend?
   (*d*) Diane had 60 p. She spent 20 p.
        What fraction did she spend?

Exercise 3

Copy each pair of fractions.
Fill in the missing numerators.

1.

$$\frac{1}{2} = \frac{\boxed{?}}{4}$$

3.

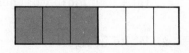

$$\frac{3}{6} = \frac{\boxed{?}}{2}$$

2.

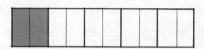

$$\frac{1}{5} = \frac{\boxed{?}}{10}$$

4.

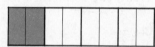

$$\frac{2}{8} = \frac{\boxed{?}}{4}$$

Exercise 4

A Copy these. Fill in the missing numbers.

1.
$$\frac{1}{2} = \frac{\boxed{?}}{4}$$
($\times 2$ on top, $\times 2$ on bottom)

7.
$$\frac{2}{3} = \frac{8}{\boxed{?}}$$

2.
$$\frac{1}{5} = \frac{2}{\boxed{?}}$$
($\times 2$ on top, $\times 2$ on bottom)

8.
$$\frac{3}{4} = \frac{\boxed{?}}{12}$$

3.
$$\frac{1}{3} = \frac{\boxed{?}}{9}$$
($\times 3$ on top, $\times 3$ on bottom)

9.
$$\frac{3}{5} = \frac{\boxed{?}}{15}$$

4.
$$\frac{3}{4} = \frac{6}{\boxed{?}}$$
($\times 2$ on top, $\times 2$ on bottom)

10.
$$\frac{1}{6} = \frac{5}{\boxed{?}}$$

5.
$$\frac{2}{5} = \frac{\boxed{?}}{15}$$
($\times 3$ on top, $\times 3$ on bottom)

11.
$$\frac{5}{7} = \frac{\boxed{?}}{14}$$

6.
$$\frac{3}{7} = \frac{6}{\boxed{?}}$$

12.
$$\frac{7}{8} = \frac{14}{\boxed{?}}$$

13. $\dfrac{7}{8} = \dfrac{35}{\boxed{?}}$ **15.** $\dfrac{4}{9} = \dfrac{20}{\boxed{?}}$

14. $\dfrac{3}{10} = \dfrac{\boxed{?}}{50}$

B Copy these. Fill in the missing numbers.

1.
$$\overset{\div 3}{\dfrac{3}{6}} = \dfrac{1}{\boxed{?}}$$
$\div 3$

5.
$$\overset{\div 6}{\dfrac{6}{18}} = \dfrac{\boxed{?}}{3}$$
$\div 6$

2.
$$\overset{\div 2}{\dfrac{2}{8}} = \dfrac{\boxed{?}}{4}$$
$\div 2$

6. $\dfrac{15}{25} = \dfrac{\boxed{?}}{5}$

3.
$$\overset{\div 2}{\dfrac{8}{10}} = \dfrac{4}{\boxed{?}}$$
$\div 2$

7. $\dfrac{10}{12} = \dfrac{5}{\boxed{?}}$

4.
$$\overset{\div 5}{\dfrac{5}{20}} = \dfrac{1}{\boxed{?}}$$
$\div 5$

8. $\dfrac{20}{30} = \dfrac{\boxed{?}}{3}$

54

9. $\dfrac{18}{24} = \dfrac{3}{\boxed{?}}$

13. $\dfrac{27}{36} = \dfrac{\boxed{?}}{\boxed{?}}$

10. $\dfrac{8}{16} = \dfrac{1}{\boxed{?}}$

14. $\dfrac{14}{35} = \dfrac{\boxed{?}}{\boxed{?}}$

11. $\dfrac{8}{14} = \dfrac{\boxed{?}}{\boxed{?}}$

15. $\dfrac{20}{36} = \dfrac{\boxed{?}}{\boxed{?}}$

12. $\dfrac{15}{40} = \dfrac{\boxed{?}}{\boxed{?}}$

Exercise 5

1. (a) There were 8 sweets. Ann ate half of them. How many did she eat?

   (b) There were 8 sweets. Don ate 2 quarters of them. How many did he eat?

   (c) Copy and complete:

   $$\frac{1}{2} = \frac{\boxed{?}}{4}$$

2. (a) $\frac{1}{3}$ of 12 cars were red. How many were red?

   (b) If $\frac{2}{6}$ of 12 cars were red, how many were red?

   (c) Copy and complete:

   $$\frac{1}{3} = \frac{\boxed{?}}{6}$$

3. (*a*) Bill used 1 quarter of 16 sheets of paper. How many sheets did he use?

(*b*) Sophie used 2 eighths of 16 sheets of paper. How many did she use?

(*c*) Copy and complete:

$$\frac{1}{4} = \frac{\boxed{?}}{8}$$

Exercise 6

Copy and complete to make sets of equivalent fractions:

1. $\dfrac{1}{2} = \dfrac{\boxed{?}}{4} = \dfrac{\boxed{?}}{6} = \dfrac{4}{\boxed{?}} = \dfrac{\boxed{?}}{10} = \dfrac{6}{12} = \dfrac{7}{\boxed{?}} = \dfrac{\boxed{?}}{16}$

2. $\dfrac{1}{3} = \dfrac{\boxed{?}}{6} = \dfrac{3}{\boxed{?}} = \dfrac{\boxed{?}}{12} = \dfrac{\boxed{?}}{15} = \dfrac{\boxed{?}}{18} = \dfrac{7}{21} = \dfrac{8}{\boxed{?}}$

3. $\dfrac{2}{3} = \dfrac{\boxed{?}}{6} = \dfrac{\boxed{?}}{9} = \dfrac{8}{\boxed{?}} = \dfrac{\boxed{?}}{15} = \dfrac{12}{\boxed{?}} = \dfrac{14}{\boxed{?}} = \dfrac{16}{\boxed{?}}$

4. $\dfrac{1}{4} = \dfrac{2}{\boxed{?}} = \dfrac{\boxed{?}}{12} = \dfrac{\boxed{?}}{16} = \dfrac{5}{\boxed{?}} = \dfrac{\boxed{?}}{24} = \dfrac{\boxed{?}}{28} = \dfrac{\boxed{?}}{32}$

5. $\dfrac{3}{4} = \dfrac{6}{\boxed{?}} = \dfrac{\boxed{?}}{12} = \dfrac{12}{\boxed{?}} = \dfrac{15}{\boxed{?}} = \dfrac{\boxed{?}}{24} = \dfrac{\boxed{?}}{28} = \dfrac{\boxed{?}}{32}$

6. $\dfrac{2}{5} = \dfrac{\boxed{?}}{10} = \dfrac{6}{\boxed{?}} = \dfrac{8}{\boxed{?}} = \dfrac{\boxed{?}}{25} = \dfrac{12}{\boxed{?}} = \dfrac{\boxed{?}}{35} = \dfrac{16}{\boxed{?}}$

Exercise 7

A Copy these fractions. Fill in the missing numbers to make the fractions equivalent.

1. $\dfrac{1}{2} = \dfrac{\boxed{?}}{8}$

2. $\dfrac{1}{5} = \dfrac{3}{\boxed{?}}$

3. $\dfrac{3}{5} = \dfrac{\boxed{?}}{20}$

4. $\dfrac{1}{6} = \dfrac{\boxed{?}}{12}$

5. $\dfrac{5}{6} = \dfrac{\boxed{?}}{12}$

6. $\dfrac{1}{7} = \dfrac{2}{\boxed{?}}$

7. $\dfrac{3}{7} = \dfrac{\boxed{?}}{21}$

8. $\dfrac{2}{9} = \dfrac{4}{\boxed{?}}$

9. $\dfrac{5}{8} = \dfrac{\boxed{?}}{16}$

10. $\dfrac{2}{7} = \dfrac{8}{\boxed{?}}$

11. $\dfrac{2}{4} = \dfrac{1}{\boxed{?}}$

12. $\dfrac{4}{6} = \dfrac{\boxed{?}}{3}$

13. $\dfrac{5}{10} = \dfrac{\boxed{?}}{2}$

14. $\dfrac{6}{8} = \dfrac{3}{\boxed{?}}$

15. $\dfrac{7}{14} = \dfrac{1}{\boxed{?}}$

16. $\dfrac{15}{20} = \dfrac{\boxed{?}}{4}$

17. $\dfrac{3}{10} = \dfrac{\boxed{?}}{40}$

18. $\dfrac{5}{9} = \dfrac{\boxed{?}}{36}$

19. $\dfrac{10}{12} = \dfrac{5}{\boxed{?}}$

20. $\dfrac{40}{50} = \dfrac{\boxed{?}}{5}$

B Give the simplest equivalent fraction for each of these:

1. $\dfrac{4}{8}$

2. $\dfrac{4}{12}$

3. $\dfrac{6}{10}$

4. $\dfrac{4}{6}$

5. $\dfrac{8}{14}$

6. $\dfrac{8}{16}$

7. $\dfrac{10}{16}$

8. $\dfrac{9}{15}$

9. $\dfrac{14}{21}$

10. $\dfrac{16}{24}$

11. $\dfrac{15}{25}$

12. $\dfrac{20}{24}$

13. $\dfrac{18}{30}$ **15.** $\dfrac{10}{35}$ **17.** $\dfrac{12}{28}$ **19.** $\dfrac{12}{42}$

14. $\dfrac{18}{27}$ **16.** $\dfrac{50}{60}$ **18.** $\dfrac{8}{26}$ **20.** $\dfrac{40}{56}$

Exercise 8

A 1.

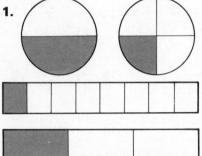

Which is bigger, $\dfrac{1}{2}$ or $\dfrac{1}{4}$?

Which is bigger, $\dfrac{1}{3}$ or $\dfrac{1}{8}$?

B Write which is bigger:

1. $\dfrac{1}{2}$ or $\dfrac{1}{8}$ **6.** $\dfrac{1}{8}$ or $\dfrac{1}{5}$ **11.** $\dfrac{1}{10}$ or $\dfrac{1}{2}$

2. $\dfrac{1}{2}$ or $\dfrac{1}{3}$ **7.** $\dfrac{1}{3}$ or $\dfrac{1}{10}$ **12.** $\dfrac{1}{8}$ or $\dfrac{1}{10}$

3. $\dfrac{1}{5}$ or $\dfrac{1}{2}$ **8.** $\dfrac{1}{6}$ or $\dfrac{1}{8}$ **13.** $\dfrac{1}{5}$ or $\dfrac{1}{6}$

4. $\dfrac{1}{3}$ or $\dfrac{1}{4}$ **9.** $\dfrac{1}{10}$ or $\dfrac{1}{5}$ **14.** $\dfrac{1}{4}$ or $\dfrac{1}{10}$

5. $\dfrac{1}{8}$ or $\dfrac{1}{4}$ **10.** $\dfrac{1}{4}$ or $\dfrac{1}{5}$ **15.** $\dfrac{1}{12}$ or $\dfrac{1}{10}$

C 1. Alan divided his chocolate bar into tenths. Pat divided the same sort of chocolate bar into eighths.
Who had the bigger pieces?

2. There were 20 sweets. Jean ate $\frac{3}{4}$ of them. David ate $\frac{3}{5}$ of another 20 sweets.
Who ate the most sweets?

3. Ken and Lenka had the same amount of money. Lenka spent 5 eighths of her money. Ken spent 5 sixths of his money.
Who spent the most money?

Exercise 9

A Copy and complete:

1. Which is bigger, $\frac{2}{3}$ or $\frac{5}{6}$?

$$\frac{2}{3} = \frac{\boxed{?}}{6} \qquad \text{and} \qquad \frac{5}{6} = \frac{\boxed{?}}{6}$$

$$\text{so} \qquad \frac{2}{3} < \frac{5}{6}$$

2. Which is bigger, $\frac{7}{8}$ or $\frac{3}{4}$?

$$\frac{7}{8} = \frac{\boxed{?}}{8} \qquad \text{and} \qquad \frac{3}{4} = \frac{\boxed{?}}{8}$$

$$\text{so} \qquad \boxed{?} > \boxed{?}$$

3. Which is bigger, $\frac{4}{5}$ or $\frac{7}{10}$?

$$\frac{4}{5} = \frac{\boxed{?}}{10} \qquad \text{and} \qquad \frac{7}{10} = \frac{\boxed{?}}{10}$$

$$\text{so} \qquad \frac{4}{5} \boxed{?} \frac{7}{10}$$

B Copy these, but put a sign $<$, $>$ or $=$ in place of each question mark to make them true:

1. $\dfrac{1}{4}$? $\dfrac{3}{4}$

2. $\dfrac{3}{4}$? $\dfrac{1}{2}$

3. $\dfrac{3}{6}$? $\dfrac{1}{3}$

4. $\dfrac{1}{2}$? $\dfrac{3}{6}$

5. $\dfrac{1}{2}$? $\dfrac{5}{8}$

6. $\dfrac{3}{5}$? $\dfrac{6}{10}$

7. $\dfrac{6}{8}$? $\dfrac{3}{4}$

8. $\dfrac{2}{4}$? $\dfrac{5}{8}$

9. $\dfrac{5}{10}$? $\dfrac{3}{5}$

10. $\dfrac{3}{4}$? $\dfrac{5}{8}$

11. $\dfrac{8}{12}$? $\dfrac{2}{3}$

12. $\dfrac{7}{12}$? $\dfrac{3}{4}$

13. $\dfrac{5}{6}$? $\dfrac{7}{12}$

14. $\dfrac{1}{3}$? $\dfrac{2}{6}$

15. $\dfrac{2}{3}$? $\dfrac{5}{6}$

Exercise 10

For each question, put the fractions in order of size with the smallest first:

1. $\dfrac{2}{5}$, $\dfrac{3}{10}$ and $\dfrac{7}{20}$

2. $\dfrac{1}{2}$, $\dfrac{3}{4}$ and $\dfrac{5}{8}$

3. $\dfrac{5}{6}$, $\dfrac{2}{3}$ and $\dfrac{11}{12}$

4. $\dfrac{13}{16}$, $\dfrac{7}{8}$ and $\dfrac{3}{4}$

5. $\dfrac{3}{8}$, $\dfrac{1}{2}$ and $\dfrac{5}{16}$

60

Exercise 11

The shaded circles show that

$$\frac{5}{3} = 1\frac{2}{3} \leftarrow \text{a mixed number}$$

$$\uparrow$$

an improper fraction

This line also shows that $\frac{5}{3} = 1\frac{2}{3}$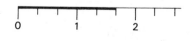

1. How many quarters are there in $1\frac{1}{4}$?

2. How many thirds are there in $2\frac{2}{3}$?

3. How many fifths are there in 2?

4. How many fifths are there in $2\frac{2}{5}$?

5. How many tenths are there in $1\frac{7}{10}$?

6. $4\dfrac{1}{4} = \dfrac{\boxed{?}}{4}$

7. $\dfrac{\boxed{?}}{6} = 2$

8. $1\dfrac{3}{8} = \dfrac{\boxed{?}}{8}$

9. $\dfrac{13}{2} = \boxed{?}$

10. $4\dfrac{2}{3} = \dfrac{\boxed{?}}{3}$

Exercise 12

A Change these mixed numbers into improper fractions:

1. $2\dfrac{1}{2} = \dfrac{\boxed{?}}{2}$

2. $1\dfrac{1}{3} = \dfrac{\boxed{?}}{3}$

3. $1\dfrac{3}{4} = \dfrac{\boxed{?}}{4}$

4. $3\dfrac{1}{2} = \dfrac{\boxed{?}}{2}$

5. $2\dfrac{1}{3} = \dfrac{\boxed{?}}{3}$

6. $3\dfrac{3}{4} = \dfrac{\boxed{?}}{4}$

7. $2\dfrac{3}{5} = \dfrac{\boxed{?}}{5}$

8. $1\dfrac{5}{8} = \dfrac{\boxed{?}}{8}$

9. $3\dfrac{1}{5} = \dfrac{\boxed{?}}{5}$

10. $1\dfrac{5}{6} = \dfrac{\boxed{?}}{6}$

11. $2\dfrac{5}{6} = \dfrac{\boxed{?}}{6}$

12. $2\dfrac{3}{7} = \dfrac{\boxed{?}}{7}$

13. $4\dfrac{2}{7} = \dfrac{\boxed{?}}{7}$

14. $3\dfrac{4}{9} = \dfrac{\boxed{?}}{9}$

15. $5\dfrac{3}{10} = \dfrac{\boxed{?}}{10}$

16. $3\dfrac{3}{8} = \dfrac{\boxed{?}}{8}$ **18.** $7\dfrac{1}{4} = \dfrac{\boxed{?}}{4}$ **20.** $4\dfrac{7}{8} = \dfrac{\boxed{?}}{8}$

17. $6\dfrac{4}{5} = \dfrac{\boxed{?}}{5}$ **19.** $8\dfrac{2}{3} = \dfrac{\boxed{?}}{3}$

B Change these improper fractions into mixed numbers:

1. $\dfrac{3}{2}$ **5.** $\dfrac{9}{2}$ **9.** $\dfrac{17}{3}$ **13.** $\dfrac{25}{8}$ **17.** $\dfrac{25}{12}$

2. $\dfrac{5}{4}$ **6.** $\dfrac{19}{6}$ **10.** $\dfrac{11}{4}$ **14.** $\dfrac{31}{6}$ **18.** $\dfrac{33}{4}$

3. $\dfrac{14}{5}$ **7.** $\dfrac{37}{10}$ **11.** $\dfrac{37}{5}$ **15.** $\dfrac{15}{2}$ **19.** $\dfrac{23}{3}$

4. $\dfrac{10}{3}$ **8.** $\dfrac{21}{8}$ **12.** $\dfrac{25}{7}$ **16.** $\dfrac{13}{3}$ **20.** $\dfrac{26}{7}$

Exercise 13

A Write as mixed numbers:

1. 11 halves	**5.** 13 sixths	**9.** 16 sevenths
2. 5 thirds	**6.** 9 fifths	**10.** 26 ninths
3. 9 quarters	**7.** 21 tenths	**11.** 19 quarters
4. 15 eighths	**8.** 35 eighths	**12.** 29 sixths

B Write as improper fractions:

1. Three and two-thirds	**6.** One and three-eighths
2. One and two-fifths	**7.** Four and three-tenths
3. Two and six-sevenths	**8.** Three and five-sixths
4. Four and a quarter	**9.** Six and five-eighths
5. Seven and a half	**10.** Seven and three-quarters

Exercise 14

Write as whole numbers:

A
1. 8 halves
2. 6 thirds
3. 15 fifths
4. 15 thirds
5. 12 quarters

6. 16 eighths
7. 24 sixths
8. 16 quarters
9. 50 tenths
10. 40 eighths

11. 42 sixths
12. 42 sevenths
13. 63 ninths
14. 35 fifths
15. 24 twelfths

B

1. $\dfrac{6}{2}$
2. $\dfrac{12}{3}$
3. $\dfrac{8}{4}$

4. $\dfrac{20}{5}$
5. $\dfrac{20}{4}$
6. $\dfrac{24}{8}$

7. $\dfrac{60}{10}$
8. $\dfrac{30}{6}$
9. $\dfrac{35}{7}$

10. $\dfrac{36}{9}$
11. $\dfrac{45}{5}$
12. $\dfrac{54}{6}$

13. $\dfrac{36}{12}$
14. $\dfrac{48}{8}$
15. $\dfrac{18}{3}$

Exercise 15

$\dfrac{1}{3}$ of 6 = 2

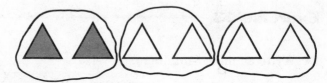

$6 \times \dfrac{1}{3}$ = 6 thirds = 2

$6 \times \dfrac{1}{3}$ = $\dfrac{6}{3}$ = 2

Three people share a bar of chocolate.
There were 12 squares altogether.
Yin ate $\frac{1}{3}$ of the bar.

Bob ate $\frac{1}{4}$ of the bar.

Chris ate $\frac{1}{6}$ of the bar.

1. Write down the number of squares each person ate. Set out your work like this:

Yin ate $\frac{1}{3}$ of 12 squares = $\boxed{?}$ squares

Bob ate $\frac{1}{4}$ of 12 squares = $\boxed{?}$ squares

Chris ate $\frac{1}{6}$ of 12 squares = $\boxed{?}$ squares

2. How many squares were left?

3. What fraction of the bar of chocolate was left?

Exercise 16 ▬▬▬▬▬▬▬▬▬▬▬▬▬▬▬ **M**

Copy these and ring each fraction:

e.g. $\frac{1}{4}$

1. $\frac{1}{3}$

2. $\frac{1}{2}$

3. $\frac{2}{3}$

4. $\frac{3}{4}$

5. $\dfrac{1}{5}$ 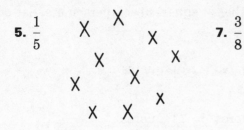   **7.** $\dfrac{3}{8}$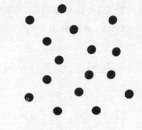

6. $\dfrac{3}{5}$ 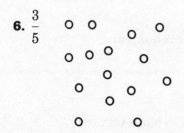   **8.** $\dfrac{7}{10}$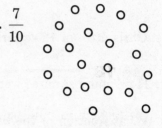

Exercise 17

A **1.** (*a*) Find one-quarter of 20 sweets.
     (*b*) Find three-quarters of 20 sweets.

   2. (*a*) Find $\frac{1}{5}$ of 15 stamps.
     (*b*) Find $\frac{4}{5}$ of 15 stamps.

   3. (*a*) What is $\frac{1}{3}$ of 12 eggs?
     (*b*) Find $\frac{2}{3}$ of 12 eggs.

   4. (*a*) Find one-sixth of 24 h.
     (*b*) What is five-sixths of 24 h?

   5. (*a*) Find $\frac{1}{8}$ of 16 m.
     (*b*) Find $\frac{5}{8}$ of 16 m.

B **1.** Find $\frac{1}{2}$ of 22 boys.

   2. Find $\frac{2}{3}$ of 15 girls.

   3. What is $\frac{3}{4}$ of 12 bananas?

   4. Find three-fifths of 30 km.

66

5. Find $\frac{5}{6}$ of 36 h.

6. What is $\frac{3}{7}$ of 14 days?

7. What is four-sevenths of 35 weeks?

8. Find $\frac{3}{8}$ of 32 cakes.

9. Find $\frac{7}{8}$ of 48 s.

10. Find $\frac{3}{10}$ of 70 cm.

Exercise 18

A **1.** Write $\frac{1}{2}$ cm in millimetres.

2. Write half a minute in seconds.

3. Write $\frac{1}{4}$ of an hour in minutes.

4. Write one-third of a day in hours.

5. What is $\frac{1}{5}$ of £1 in pence?

6. Write $\frac{3}{4}$ of a day in hours.

7. Write $\frac{2}{3}$ of an hour in minutes.

8. What is $\frac{3}{10}$ of £1 in pence?

9. How many metres are there in $\frac{2}{5}$ of 1 km?

10. How many centimetres are there in $\frac{3}{4}$ m?

B Copy and complete these sentences by filling in the missing word. Choose the missing word from this set of words:

{half, third, quarter, fifth, sixth, seventh, eighth, ninth, tenth}

1. There are 30 min in $\boxed{?}$ an hour.

2. There are 20 s in a $\boxed{?}$ of a minute.

3. 10 cm is a $\boxed{?}$ of a metre.

67

4. One day is a $\boxed{?}$ of a week.

5. There are 25 p in a $\boxed{?}$ of £1.

6. There are 4 h in a $\boxed{?}$ of a day.

7. One $\boxed{?}$ of a day is 12 h.

8. 2 mm is one $\boxed{?}$ of 1 cm.

Exercise 19

The pie chart shows the sports enjoyed by 48 people.

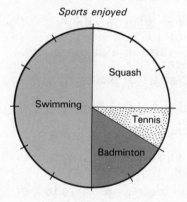

Sports enjoyed

1. What fraction liked swimming?

2. What fraction liked squash?

3. What fraction liked tennis?

4. What fraction liked badminton?

5. How many liked swimming?

6. How many liked squash?

7. How many liked tennis?

8. How many liked badminton?

Exercise 20

1. Find $\frac{1}{2}$ of 38 p.

2. What is $\frac{1}{4}$ of 48 p?

3. Find $\frac{1}{3}$ of £24.

4. Find $\frac{1}{5}$ of £45.

5. What is $\frac{1}{8}$ of £72?

6. Find $\frac{1}{9}$ of 63 p.

7. Find $\frac{1}{2}$ of £5.

8. Find $\frac{1}{3}$ of £7.50.

9. What is $\frac{1}{8}$ of £9.12?

10. Find $\frac{2}{3}$ of 27 p.

11. What is $\frac{4}{5}$ of £35?

12. Find $\frac{3}{10}$ of £2.

Exercise 21

1. Draw straight lines to $\frac{1}{2}$ the given length:
(a) 8 cm   (b) 100 mm (c) 18 cm   (d) 11 cm   (e) 19 cm

2. Draw straight lines to $\frac{1}{3}$ the given length:
(a) 30 cm   (b) 24 cm   (c) 270 mm (d) 21 cm   (e) 195 mm

3. Draw straight lines to $\frac{2}{3}$ the given length:
(a) 18 cm   (b) 120 mm (c) 15 cm   (d) 60 mm   (e) 135 mm

4. Draw straight lines to $\frac{3}{4}$ the given length:
(a) 16 cm   (b) 12 cm   (c) 60 mm   (d) 140 mm (e) 10 cm

Exercise 22

Carry out these additions:

1. $\dfrac{5}{11} + \dfrac{4}{11}$

2. $\dfrac{3}{12} + \dfrac{4}{12}$

3. $\dfrac{6}{13} + \dfrac{5}{13}$

4. $\dfrac{7}{15} + \dfrac{6}{15}$

5. $\dfrac{11}{20} + \dfrac{8}{20}$

6. $\dfrac{4}{10} + \dfrac{3}{10}$

69

7. $\dfrac{3}{5} + \dfrac{1}{5}$ **9.** $\dfrac{11}{16} + \dfrac{2}{16}$ **11.** $\dfrac{51}{100} + \dfrac{36}{100}$

8. $\dfrac{2}{8} + \dfrac{5}{8}$ **10.** $\dfrac{3}{16} + \dfrac{8}{16}$ **12.** $\dfrac{28}{100} + \dfrac{49}{100}$

Exercise 23

Carry out these additions.
Simplify your answers.

1. $\dfrac{3}{8} + \dfrac{1}{8}$ **5.** $\dfrac{5}{16} + \dfrac{3}{16}$ **9.** $\dfrac{7}{20} + \dfrac{3}{20}$

2. $\dfrac{1}{8} + \dfrac{5}{8}$ **6.** $\dfrac{5}{16} + \dfrac{1}{16}$ **10.** $\dfrac{3}{20} + \dfrac{1}{20}$

3. $\dfrac{1}{10} + \dfrac{3}{10}$ **7.** $\dfrac{9}{16} + \dfrac{3}{16}$ **11.** $\dfrac{11}{20} + \dfrac{1}{20}$

4. $\dfrac{7}{10} + \dfrac{1}{10}$ **8.** $\dfrac{7}{16} + \dfrac{3}{16}$ **12.** $\dfrac{3}{8} + \dfrac{5}{8}$

Exercise 24

Carry out these subtractions:

1. $\dfrac{2}{3} - \dfrac{1}{3}$ **4.** $\dfrac{6}{7} - \dfrac{3}{7}$ **7.** $\dfrac{7}{9} - \dfrac{3}{9}$

2. $\dfrac{4}{5} - \dfrac{3}{5}$ **5.** $\dfrac{5}{7} - \dfrac{1}{7}$ **8.** $\dfrac{9}{10} - \dfrac{6}{10}$

3. $\dfrac{5}{6} - \dfrac{4}{6}$ **6.** $\dfrac{7}{8} - \dfrac{2}{8}$ **9.** $\dfrac{11}{12} - \dfrac{6}{12}$

10. $\dfrac{13}{16} - \dfrac{6}{16}$ **11.** $\dfrac{11}{16} - \dfrac{2}{16}$ **12.** $\dfrac{18}{20} - \dfrac{7}{20}$

Exercise 25

Carry out these subtractions.
Simplify your answers.

1. $\dfrac{5}{6} - \dfrac{1}{6}$ **5.** $\dfrac{9}{10} - \dfrac{1}{10}$ **9.** $\dfrac{11}{12} - \dfrac{5}{12}$

2. $\dfrac{5}{6} - \dfrac{2}{6}$ **6.** $\dfrac{7}{10} - \dfrac{3}{10}$ **10.** $\dfrac{15}{16} - \dfrac{7}{16}$

3. $\dfrac{5}{8} - \dfrac{1}{8}$ **7.** $\dfrac{8}{10} - \dfrac{3}{10}$ **11.** $\dfrac{13}{16} - \dfrac{9}{16}$

4. $\dfrac{7}{8} - \dfrac{1}{8}$ **8.** $\dfrac{8}{9} - \dfrac{2}{9}$ **12.** $\dfrac{15}{16} - \dfrac{3}{16}$

Exercise 26

Carry out these subtractions:

1. $1 - \dfrac{1}{2}$ **5.** $1 - \dfrac{7}{10}$ **9.** $1 - \dfrac{5}{12}$

2. $1 - \dfrac{3}{4}$ **6.** $1 - \dfrac{3}{5}$ **10.** $1 - \dfrac{7}{16}$

3. $1 - \dfrac{5}{8}$ **7.** $1 - \dfrac{9}{10}$ **11.** $1 - \dfrac{5}{6}$

4. $1 - \dfrac{3}{8}$ **8.** $1 - \dfrac{1}{12}$ **12.** $1 - \dfrac{1}{6}$

Exercise 27

Carry out these multiplications:

1. $4 \times \dfrac{1}{5}$

2. $4 \times \dfrac{2}{5}$

3. $6 \times \dfrac{3}{5}$

4. $7 \times \dfrac{1}{2}$

5. $2 \times \dfrac{2}{3}$

6. $5 \times \dfrac{3}{4}$

7. $5 \times \dfrac{3}{8}$

8. $7 \times \dfrac{5}{6}$

9. $7 \times \dfrac{9}{10}$

10. $9 \times \dfrac{7}{10}$

5 Angles, Parallels and Constructions

Exercise 1

Write whether each angle is an acute angle, an obtuse angle, a reflex angle, a right angle or a straight angle:

1.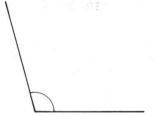

5.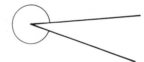

2.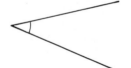

6.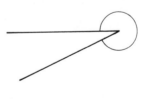

3.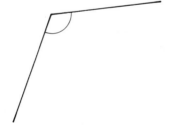

7.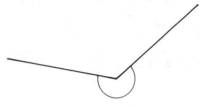

4.

8.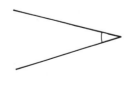

Exercise 2

Write whether the given angle is an acute angle, an obtuse angle, a reflex angle, a right angle or a straight angle:

1. 50°	**5.** 182°	**9.** 180°
2. 135°	**6.** 108°	**10.** 327°
3. 72°	**7.** 90°	**11.** 264°
4. 215°	**8.** 23°	**12.** 99°

Exercise 3

Measure these angles. Estimate each one first.

1.

3.

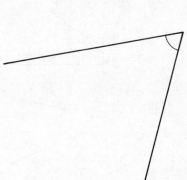

2.

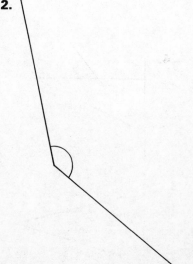

4.

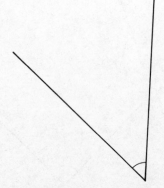

5.

Exercise 4

A Try to do these calculations in your head:

1. $360° - 60°$
2. $360° - 120°$
3. $360° - 40°$
4. $360° - 90°$
5. $360° - 25°$
6. $360° - 140°$
7. $360° - 85°$
8. $360° - 125°$
9. $360° - 170°$
10. $360° - 110°$
11. $360° - 45°$
12. $360° - 105°$
13. $360° - 175°$
14. $360° - 95°$
15. $360° - 145°$

B Measure these angles. All of them are bigger than 180°. (The calculations above may help.)

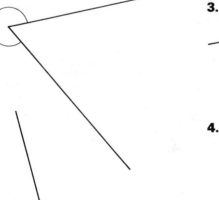

1.

2.

3.

4.

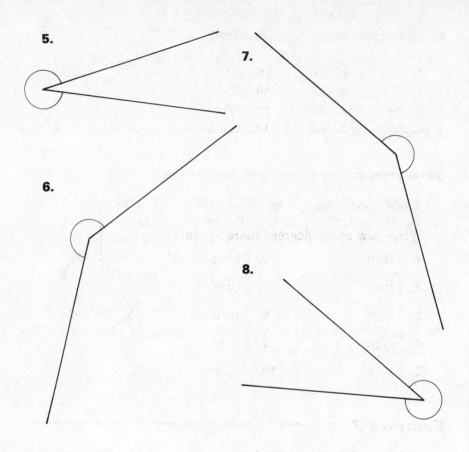

5.

7.

6.

8.

Exercise 5

A Try to do these calculations in your head:

1.	$360° - 330°$	**13.**	$360° - 195°$
2.	$360° - 260°$	**14.**	$360° - 215°$
3.	$360° - 200°$	**15.**	$360° - 325°$
4.	$360° - 310°$	**16.**	$360° - 315°$
5.	$360° - 270°$	**17.**	$360° - 275°$
6.	$360° - 210°$	**18.**	$360° - 225°$
7.	$360° - 230°$	**19.**	$360° - 205°$
8.	$360° - 340°$	**20.**	$360° - 335°$
9.	$360° - 305°$	**21.**	$360° - 265°$
10.	$360° - 255°$	**22.**	$360° - 235°$
11.	$360° - 295°$	**23.**	$360° - 345°$
12.	$360° - 245°$	**24.**	$360° - 285°$

B Draw these angles and label them:

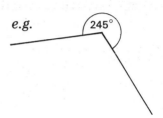
e.g.

1. 330°   **5.** 190°   **9.** 195°
2. 260°   **6.** 305°   **10.** 225°
3. 200°   **7.** 255°   **11.** 345°
4. 230°   **8.** 295°   **12.** 285°

Exercise 6

A full turn = 360°.

Write how many degrees there are in:

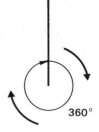

1. $\frac{1}{2}$ turn   **6.** $\frac{5}{8}$ turn

2. $\frac{1}{4}$ turn   **7.** $\frac{7}{8}$ turn

3. $\frac{3}{4}$ turn   **8.** $\frac{1}{6}$ turn

4. $\frac{1}{8}$ turn   **9.** $\frac{5}{6}$ turn

5. $\frac{3}{8}$ turn   **10.** $\frac{1}{12}$ turn

Exercise 7

1. In the diagram, ∠ DBC has been marked.

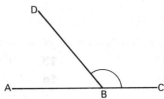

Copy the diagram and mark angle DBC.
Now mark angle DBA using a different colour.

2. Copy the diagram and mark angle PYZ.

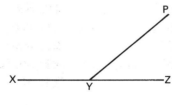

3. For each of the given diagrams write the angle that has been marked.

(a)

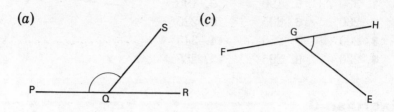

(c)

(b)

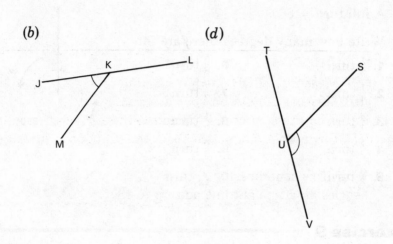

(d)

Exercise 8

1. (a) Measure ∠ WYZ.
   (b) Measure ∠ WYX.

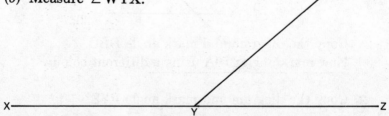

(c) Find the sum of the two angles.

(d) Write what you notice about the sum of ∠ WYZ and ∠ WYX.

78

2. (*a*) Draw any straight line. Label it AB.

(*b*) Draw any straight line, PQ, to meet AB where Q lies on AB.

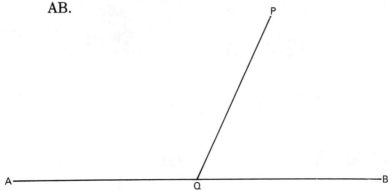

(*c*) Measure ∠ PQB on your diagram.

(*d*) Measure ∠ PQA on your diagram.

(*e*) Find the sum of ∠ PQB and ∠ PQA.

(*f*) Write what you notice about the sum of the two angles.

3. Copy this sentence:

Angles on a straight line add up to 180°.

Exercise 9

Greek letters are often used to stand for angles.

We shall use the letter θ ('theta').

Calculate the missing angles. DO NOT MEASURE.

e.g.

$\underline{\underline{\theta = 130°}}$

θ

50°

1.

θ

30°

2.

140°

θ

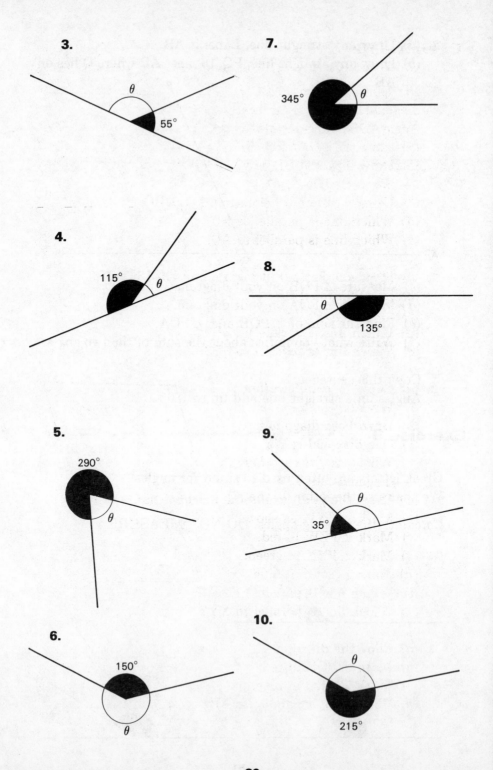

3.

θ

55°

7.

345° θ

4.

115° θ

8.

θ

135°

5.

290°

θ

9.

θ

35°

6.

150°

θ

10.

θ

215°

Exercise 10

1. In parallelogram ABCD, diagonal BD has been drawn. Angle ADB has been marked.
   (a) Copy the parallelogram.
   (b) Draw diagonal BD and mark ∠ ADB.
   (c) Using a different colour, mark ∠ DBC.
   (d) Which line is parallel to AB.
   (e) Which line is parallel to AD.

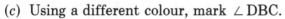

2. (a) Draw another parallelogram and label it PQRS.
   (b) Draw diagonal PR.
   (c) Mark angle PRS.
   (d) Which line is parallel to SR?
   (e) Which line is parallel to SP?

3. (a) Copy parallelogram WXYZ.
   (b) Draw both diagonals.
   (c) One diagonal is WY. What is the other diagonal called?
   (d) Label the point where the diagonals cross as P.
   (e) Mark ∠ PXW as shown.
   (f) Mark ∠ PZW in red.
   (g) Mark ∠ PYX in green.
   (h) Mark ∠ YWZ in blue.
   (i) Which line is parallel to XW?
   (j) Which line is parallel to XY?

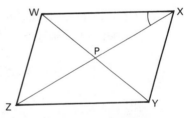

4. (a) Copy the diagram.
   (b) Mark ∠ PQB in red.
   (c) Mark ∠ CRQ in blue.
   (b) Which line is parallel to AB?

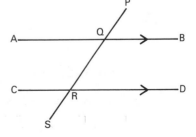

Constructions

Exercise 11

1. Draw a straight line XY, and mark a point P as shown. Using a ruler and set square construct a line that is parallel to XY and that passes through point P.

P

X————————————————Y

2. Draw a straight line JK, 40 mm long. Using a ruler and set square draw a line at K that is perpendicular to JK. Label the line KL where KL is 30 mm. Join JL. How long is JL?

3. Draw a straight line 70 mm long. Bisect the line using a pair of compasses.

4. Construct a hexagon with sides 30 mm. Label the vertices ABCDEF.

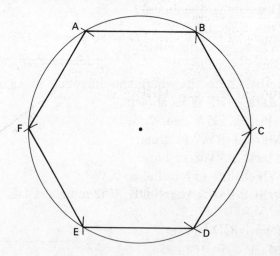

Join A to C to E and then back to A. (Use *straight* lines.)

Join B to D to F and then back to B using *straight* lines.

Colour your pattern.

Exercise 12

Use a ruler, protractor and a pair of compasses to help you to construct these triangles.
The drawings are not to the proper size.

1.

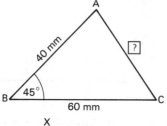

How long is AC?

2.

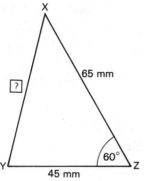

How long is XY?

3. Construct △ PQR, where PQ = 60 mm, ∠ QPR = 35° and PR = 78 mm.
   (*a*) How long is QR?
   (*b*) Find the size of ∠ QRP.

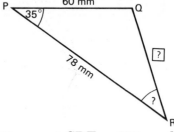

4. Construct △ CDE, where DE = 52 mm, ∠ CDE = 25°, and ∠ DEC = 110°.
How long is CD?

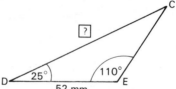

5. Construct an equilateral triangle with sides of 4 cm.

Exercise 13

Carry out these constructions. (The given drawings are not the correct size.)

1. Construct a parallelogram PQRS, where SR = 45 mm, angle RSP = 60° and SP = 30 mm.

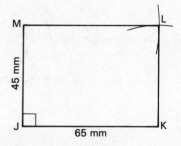

2. Construct a rectangle JKLM, where JK = 65 mm and JM = 45 mm.

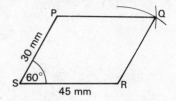

3. Construct a square with sides 45 mm long.

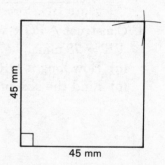

4. Construct a rhombus WXYZ, where all the sides are 50 mm and where angle XYZ = 65°.

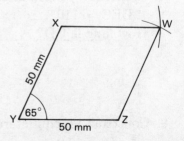

Exercise 14

Use a ruler and a pair of compasses for these constructions:

1. Construct △ABC where BC = 60 mm, BA = 65 mm and CA = 45 mm.

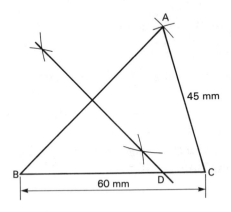

Using a pair of compasses, bisect side AB.
Let the bisector cut BC at D.
Measure BD.

2. Construct △ABC where BC = 95 mm, BA = 45 mm and CA = 75 mm.

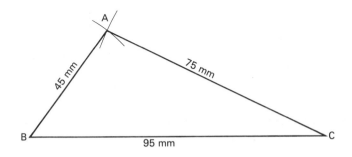

Using a pair of compasses, bisect side AB.
Let the bisector cut BC at D.
Measure BD.

Exercise 15

Draw any angle ABC.
With centre B, and any radius,
draw an arc to cut AB at D and
to cut BC at E.

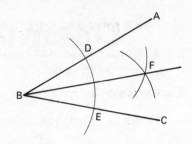

Check that your pair of compasses is set to a radius that is
greater than half of DE.

With centre at D, draw an arc between the arms and away
from B.
With centre at E, using the *same* radius, draw another arc to
cross the other at F.
Draw a straight line from B, through F. This straight line, BF,
bisects angle ABC.

Exercise 16

Construct △ABC where BC = 75 mm, AB = 70 mm and
AC = 40 mm.

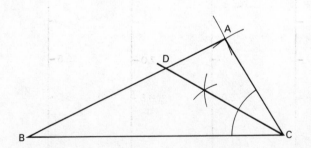

Bisect angle C using a pair of compasses.
Let the bisector meet AB at D.
Measure BD.

6 Decimals

Exercise 1

Write in words the value of the underlined digit:

e.g.   416.5̲2   Five-tenths

(*Words*: thousands, hundreds, tens, units, tenths, hundredths)

1. 56.3̲   **4.** 7̲60.5   **7.** 9814.7̲   **10.** 3246.8
2. 294̲.7   **5.** 3̲09.61   **8.** 2.81̲   **11.** 6174.25̲
3. 1.84̲   **6.** 6532̲   **9.** 18.9̲7   **12.** 0.16̲

Exercise 2 M

Carefully copy each of these scales.
Only some of the points have been numbered.
Number all the points on your drawings.

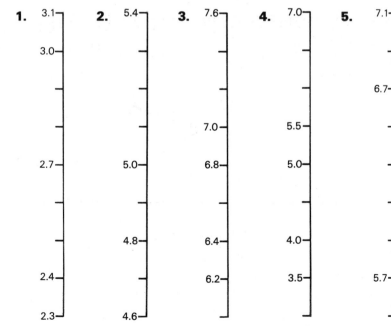

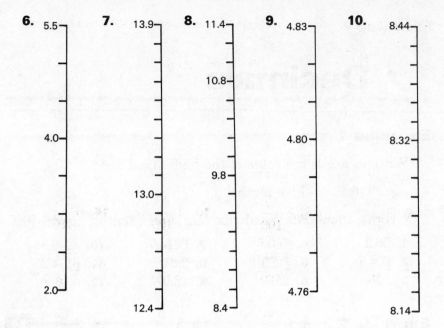

Exercise 3

Change these common fractions to decimals:

1. $\dfrac{3}{10}$

2. $\dfrac{9}{10}$

3. $\dfrac{29}{100}$

4. $\dfrac{43}{100}$

5. $\dfrac{81}{100}$

6. $\dfrac{25}{100}$

7. $\dfrac{32}{100}$

8. $\dfrac{7}{100}$

9. $\dfrac{11}{100}$

10. $\dfrac{96}{100}$

11. $\dfrac{1}{100}$

12. $\dfrac{59}{100}$

Exercise 4

Write these common fractions as decimals:

e.g. 1 $4\dfrac{3}{10} = 4.3$ *e.g. 2* $5\dfrac{49}{100} = 5.49$ *e.g. 3* $2\dfrac{7}{100} = 2.07$

1. $5\dfrac{7}{10}$ **5.** $4\dfrac{21}{100}$ **9.** $18\dfrac{63}{100}$ **13.** $36\dfrac{5}{100}$

2. $3\dfrac{9}{10}$ **6.** $8\dfrac{57}{100}$ **10.** $1\dfrac{13}{100}$ **14.** $6\dfrac{99}{100}$

3. $7\dfrac{1}{10}$ **7.** $2\dfrac{84}{100}$ **11.** $7\dfrac{3}{100}$ **15.** $12\dfrac{13}{100}$

4. $6\dfrac{4}{10}$ **8.** $9\dfrac{35}{100}$ **12.** $5\dfrac{9}{100}$ **16.** $3\dfrac{52}{100}$

Exercise 5

Change these fractions into decimals with a calculator:

1. $\dfrac{1}{2}$ **6.** $\dfrac{1}{8}$ **11.** $\dfrac{19}{20}$ **16.** $\dfrac{5}{16}$

2. $\dfrac{1}{5}$ **7.** $\dfrac{3}{8}$ **12.** $\dfrac{2}{25}$ **17.** $\dfrac{13}{16}$

3. $\dfrac{3}{5}$ **8.** $\dfrac{7}{8}$ **13.** $\dfrac{9}{25}$ **18.** $\dfrac{17}{40}$

4. $\dfrac{1}{4}$ **9.** $\dfrac{9}{20}$ **14.** $\dfrac{13}{25}$ **19.** $\dfrac{29}{40}$

5. $\dfrac{3}{4}$ **10.** $\dfrac{11}{20}$ **15.** $\dfrac{22}{25}$ **20.** $\dfrac{23}{80}$

Exercise 6

Answer these:

A **1.** 5.4 + 6.8

2. 8.5 + 2.9

3. 61.3 + 82.8

4. 7.8 + 25.9

5. 2.67 + 3.19

6. 65.3 + 8

7. 461.7 + 233.6

8. 5.15 + 7

9. 91.9 + 107.4

10. 12.6 + 83.4 + 49.8

11. 81.7 + 2.18 + 9.77

12. 22 + 3.87 + 14.5

B **1.** 8.4 − 3.7

2. 9.1 − 4.8

3. 41.6 − 17.2

4. 59.3 − 24.9

5. 7.45 − 1.86

6. 5.02 − 2.74

7. 9 − 3.4

8. 52.61 − 12.98

9. 76.43 − 49.16

10. 39.08 − 16.19

11. 47.92 − 38.6

12. 83.5 − 41.34

Exercise 7

Write these decimals correct to the nearest whole number:

1. 5.7

2. 9.2

3. 3.9

4. 14.6

5. 26.1

6. 31.8

7. 3.75

8. 5.16

9. 8.42

10. 19.78

11. 28.81

12. 52.39

Significant Figures

The number 8 has one *significant figure*.
8.23 has three significant figures.
8.23 = 8 correct to 1 s.f. (s.f. stands for significant figure).
731.5 = 700 correct to 1 s.f. In this case the zeros are not significant. 731.5 is about 700 so we use 700. 731.5 is not nearly equal to 7 so the zeros must be used.

Exercise 8

Write the given numbers correct to 1 significant figure:

e.g. 1 273.1 = 300 correct to 1 s.f.

e.g. 2   62.9 = 60 correct to 1 s.f.

e.g. 3   4.76 =   5 correct to 1 s.f.

e.g. 4   54.95 = 50 correct to 1 s.f.

1. 68.4

2. 24.1

3. 3.27

4. 8.91

5. 57.18

6. 422.7

7. 689.2

8. 357.6

9. 124.3

10. 796.8

11. 172.1

12. 87.08

13. 34.95

14. 290.5

15. 77.7

16. 535.24

17. 1.92

18. 65.96

19. 98.7

20. 971.4

Exercise 9

Estimate the answers to these.
Work with one significant figure.

e.g. 1 $4.6 \times 7 \approx 5 \times 7 = \underline{35}$

e.g. 2 $32.9 \div 6 \approx 30 \div 6 = \underline{5}$

e.g. 3 $583.7 \times 4 \approx 600 \times 4 = \underline{2400}$

1. 6.2×3

2. 7.9×5

3. $9.6 \div 5$

4. 52.5×5

5. 44.7×8

6. $37.7 \div 8$

7. $31.9 \div 5$

8. 38.3×7

9. $41.5 \div 2$

10. $57.4 \div 3$

11. 62.7×4

12. 88.2×6

13. 178.4×9

14. $761.3 \div 4$

15. $97.63 \div 4$

Exercise 10

Answer these. Check by estimating.

1. 7.6×2	**8.** 2×8.72	**15.** 2.061×3
2. 5×23.6	**9.** 5.63×3	**16.** $31.74 \div 6$
3. 41.1×6	**10.** $7.84 \div 4$	**17.** $47.05 \div 5$
4. $3.8 \div 2$	**11.** $9.462 \div 2$	**18.** $194.4 \div 8$
5. $57.6 \div 3$	**12.** $87.21 \div 3$	**19.** 7×382.8
6. 7×19.5	**13.** 4×5.15	**20.** 487.1×6
7. 38.2×8	**14.** 9×8.59	

Exercise 11

1. If a car travels 41.3 miles on 1 gal of petrol, how far does it go on 4 gal?

2. A rectangle is 6.9 cm long and 2.8 cm wide.
Find its perimeter.

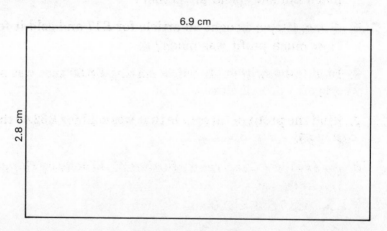

6.9 cm

2.8 cm

3. A piece of rope 13.5 m long is cut into three equal lengths. How long is each length?

4. A piece of wood is 2.44 m long. A length of 1.18 m is cut off. What length is left?

5. A can holds 2.3 ℓ of oil. How many litres will six cans hold?

Exercise 12 Money

Write each amount of money in the way it should be written:

1. 6 £	**5.** £4 36 p	**9.** £ 3.0
2. £4.73 p	**6.** £.98	**10.** 675 p
3. 184 p	**7.** 5.1 £	**11.** 500 p
4. £5.8	**8.** £0.2	**12.** £82.64 p

Exercise 13 Addition and Subtraction of Money

1. Alan spent £2.60 at one shop and £3.70 at another. How much did he spend altogether?

2. How much change do I get from £5 if I spend £1.80?

3. How much change do I get from £5 if I spend £3.65?

4. Brenda spent £4.35 at one shop and £6.90 at another. How much did she spend altogether?

5. A shopkeeper bought an article for £17 and sold it for £24. How much profit was made?

6. Find the profit on an article costing £8.50 that was sold for £14.

7. Find the profit on an article that was sold for £32.40 that cost £23.65.

8. A stereo cost £24.95 and a further £2.40 delivery charge. Find the total cost.

Exercise 14 Multiplication and Division of Money

1. A comic costs 65 p. Find the cost of two.

2. Kathy earns £2.40 an hour. How much does she earn in 4 h?

3. Ken earns £9.40 in 4 h. How much is that per hour?

4. Find the cost of five books at £3.95 each.

5. My newspapers cost £3.92 for a fortnight. Find the weekly cost.

6. Raju saved £3.45 per week for 6 weeks. How much was that?

7. Fiona's fare came to £3.90 in five days. What was the daily cost?

8. Three tins of paint cost £19.35. Find the cost of one tin if each cost the same.

Exercise 15   Miscellaneous Questions

1. A pen cost £4.85 while a book was £3.70. Find the total cost.

2. Two items cost £6.24. If one cost £4.38 how much was the other?

3. Petrol cost £16.42. How much change was there out of £20.

4. Find the cost of four bars of chocolate at £1.86 each.

5. I spent £5.76 at one shop and £9.58 at another. How much did I spend altogether?

6. On a journey, the train fare for four people was £15.68. What was the cost per person?

7. Find the cost of 5 m of material at £6.49 per metre.

8. If I saved £116.76 in six weeks. How much was that per week?

Exercise 16

Find the cost of:

1. 2 rubbers at 38 p each

2. 5 pencils at 23 p each

3. 3 bags of potatoes at 76 p per bag

4. 2 lb of apples at 29 p per pound

5. Half a dozen mugs at 97 p each

6. 2 computer games at £4.95 each

7. 4 books at £2.95 each

8. 8 m of material at £5.82 per metre

9. 3 batteries at £1.28 each

10. 7 records at £5.34 each

Exercise 17 — M

Copy and complete these invoices:

1.

				£ p
2	writing pads	@	69 p	1.38
3	packets of envelopes	@	69 p	
1	bottle of ink	@	78 p	
3	packs of cartridges	@	42 p	
1	pen	@	£4.95	
			Total cost	£

2.

				£ p
3	tins of gloss paint	@	£5.99	
2	tins of undercoat	@	£3.60	
2	paintbrushes	@	£1.75	
6	rolls of wallpaper	@	£4.80	
2	packets of paste	@	£0.78	
			Total cost	£

Revision Exercises I to VI

Revision Exercise I

1. Which of these are simple closed curves?

(a)   (b)   (c)   (d)

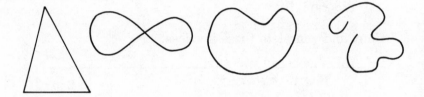

2. Show each of these sets on a Venn diagram:
   (a) The set of counting numbers less than 15.
   (b) The set of odd numbers between 20 and 30.

3. List these sets. Use curly brackets and commas:
   (a) The set of months of the year that end with the letter y.
   (b) The set of numbers that lie between 105 and 205 that divide exactly by 10.

4. Show these sets on Venn diagrams:
   (a) The set of letters in the word FRUIT = {f, r, u, i, t}
   (b) The set of multiples of 4 that are less than 30 = {4, 8, 12, 16, 20, 24, 28}

5. A Venn diagram is given. List the set using curly brackets.

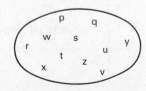

6. Copy and complete these sets:
   (a) The set of vowels = {a, ? , i, o, ? }
   (b) The set of even numbers between 49 and 75
       = {50, ? , 58, 52, 62, ? , 54, 60, ? , 68, 74, 70, ? }

7. Write the wrong member from each of these sets:
   (a) A set of trees = {oak, ash, fur, elm, beech}
   (b) The set of divisors of 18 = {1, 2, 3, 4, 6, 9, 18}

8. Here is a set of numbers: {6, 9, 10, 12, 13, 18, 20}. Write a set of numbers where the members are twice as big as the members of the set above.

9. From the given Venn diagram, list:
   (a) The set of odd numbers.
   (b) The set of numbers that divide exactly by 5.

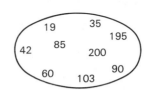

10. Copy these. Replace each box with ∈ or ∉ to make each sentence true:
    (a) 36 ? {factors of 6}
    (b) 9 ? {factors of 45}

11. Is the set of odd numbers that divide exactly by 4 an empty set?

12. How many members has the set of multiples of 8 that are less than 70?

Revision Exercise II

1. How many digits has the number 57 092?

2. Write two thousand, eight hundred and four in figures.

3. Write thirty-nine thousand in figures.

4. If 39 + ? = 100, find the missing number.

5. If 39 + ? = 1000, find the missing number.

6. Pat had 12 sweets. She ate 5 then was given 14 more. How many did she then have?

7. Harry had 437 stamps. He gave 169 away then bought another 84. How any did he then have?

8. Find 46 000 + 39 000.

9. Answer these:
   (a) 6834 + 1579
   (b) 284 + 1635 + 4097
   (c) 843 − 379
   (d) 5207 − 2938
   (e) 38 × 7
   (f) 206 × 4
   (g) 918 ÷ 2
   (h) 6234 ÷ 6

10. What must I add to 74 to make 100?

11. Find the difference between 97 and 48.

12. Find the product of 19 and 8.

13. Answer these:
    (a) 24 × 10   (b) 61 × 100   (c) 40 × 600

14. Round 356 correct to the nearest hundred.

15. Find the answer to 43 × 21.

16. Which of these numbers divide exactly by 9?
    (a) 134   (b) 207   (c) 4113   (d) 5101

Revision Exercise III

1. Draw a rectangle 50 mm by 30 mm.
   Draw its axes of bilateral symmetry.

2. Write which of these shapes have bilateral symmetry:
   (a) 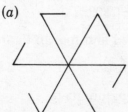   (b)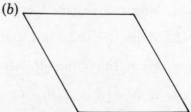

(c) 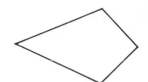 (d)

3. Write which of the shapes in question 2 have rotational symmetry.

Revision Exercise IV

1. Copy the square.   Shade $\frac{2}{3}$.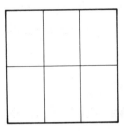

2. Draw a straight line 120 mm long.
Divide it into sixths.

3. Copy these. Fill in the missing numbers.

(a) $\dfrac{2}{3} = \dfrac{\boxed{?}}{12}$ ($\times 4$)   (b) $\dfrac{3}{4} = \dfrac{12}{\boxed{?}}$

(c) $\dfrac{10}{15} = \dfrac{\boxed{?}}{3}$

4. Simplify: (a) $\dfrac{7}{28}$ (b) $\dfrac{9}{12}$

5. Which is bigger, $\frac{1}{8}$ or $\frac{1}{12}$?

6. Which is bigger, $\frac{3}{4}$ or $\frac{7}{8}$?

7. Put the fractions $\frac{5}{8}$, $\frac{7}{16}$ and $\frac{1}{2}$ in order of size with the largest first.

8. How many eighths are there in $2\frac{3}{8}$?

9. Change $\frac{15}{4}$ into a mixed number.

10. Write $\frac{32}{8}$ as a whole number.

11. Find $\frac{1}{3}$ of 18 sweets.

12. Find $\frac{3}{4}$ of 20 apples.

13. Write $\frac{3}{4}$ of an hour in minutes.

14. Find $\frac{7}{10}$ of £3.

15. Draw a straight line $\frac{2}{5}$ of 15 cm.

16. Answer these. Simplify your answer where possible.

(a) $\dfrac{3}{8} + \dfrac{2}{8}$ (b) $\dfrac{3}{8} + \dfrac{3}{8}$ (c) $7 \times \dfrac{2}{5}$

Revision Exercise V

1. Name the type of angle shown:

2. Is an angle of 179° a reflex angle?

3. What type of angle is an angle of 201°?

4. Measure the given angle:

5. Draw an angle of 295°.

6. How many degrees are there in
(a) $\frac{3}{4}$ of a turn?
(b) $\frac{5}{12}$ of a turn?

7. Copy the diagram given below. Mark angle JKM.

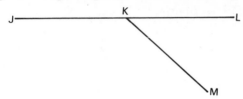

8. Calculate the missing angles:

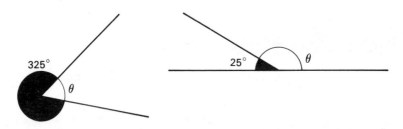

9. Draw a straight line 65 mm long.
Bisect it using a pair of compasses.

10. Construct a hexagon with sides 25 mm.

11. Using a protractor, draw an angle of 55°.
Bisect the angle using a pair of compasses.

12. Use any of your drawing instruments to help you with these constructions. The given drawings are not to the proper size.

(*a*) Construct a square with sides 40 mm.

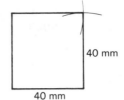

(*b*) Construct △LMN where MN = 75 mm, ∠LMN = 40° and LM = 45 mm.

Using a pair of compasses, bisect side LN.
If the bisector cuts MN at X, measure NX.

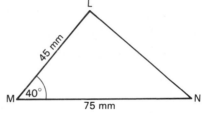

(c) Construct △CDE where DE = 70 mm, CD = 40 mm and EC = 60 mm. Using a pair of compasses, bisect ∠CDE. If the bisector cuts CE at P, measure PE.

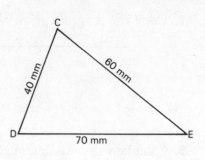

Revision Exercise VI

1. In the number 325.74, what is the value of the underlined digit?

2. Write as decimals:

(a) $\dfrac{8}{10}$ (b) $\dfrac{57}{100}$ (c) $\dfrac{9}{100}$ (d) $2\dfrac{39}{100}$ (e) $14\dfrac{85}{100}$

3. Answer these:
(a) 62.4 + 9.8   (b) 85.71 − 32.84

4. Write 26.53 correct to the nearest whole number.

5. Write these numbers correct to one significant figure:
(a) 54.8   (b) 362.9   (c) 78.04   (d) 97.6

6. Estimate the answers to these.
Work with one significant figure.
(a) 47.2 × 7   (b) 86.4 ÷ 3

7. Find the value of:
(a) 2.94 × 6   (b) 71.56 ÷ 4

8. Each side of an equilateral triangle measures 7.8 cm. Calculate its perimeter.

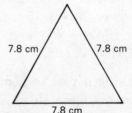

9. Find the cost of 4 pens at 79 p each.

10. I spent £2.73 at one shop and £6.89 at another. How much was that altogether?

11. If I spent £6.32 at a shop, how much change would I get out of a £10 note?

12. I paid £4.35 for three tapes. What did each tape cost?

7 Ratio

1. Draw a straight line that is twice as long as this line:

_____

2. Draw a straight line that is double the length of this line:

_____

3. Draw a straight line that is four times as long as this line:

_____

4. Draw a rectangle the same shape as this rectangle. Make each side twice as long.

5. Draw a square where each side is three times as long as each side of this square.

6. *Enlarge* the given rectangle. Make each side three times as long.

Exercise 2

How many times as big is the first quantity compared with the second?

1. £4, £2
2. 6 km, 3 km
3. 6 min, 2 min
4. 8 h, 2 h
5. 12 cm, 4 cm
6. 12 cm, 3 cm
7. 12 cm, 6 cm
8. 12 cm, 2 cm
9. 10 years, 2 years
10. 14 in, 2 in

11. 20 days, 5 days
12. 24 kg, 6 kg
13. 18 ft, 2 ft
14. 40 p, 5 p
15. £50, £5
16. 24 km, 4 km
17. 60 yd, 10 yd
18. 48 s, 6 s
19. 26 weeks, 13 weeks
20. 54 km, 9 km

Exercise 3

How many times as long is the first line compared with the second?

1. ───────────────────────────

───────────────

2. ──────────────────────────────

──────

3. ─────────────────────────────

────────

4. ────────────────────

─────

5. ──────────────────────

────────

Exercise 4

How many times as big is the first quantity compared with the second?

1. £2, 50 p
2. 1 min, 30 s
3. 1 h, 15 min
4. 2 years, 6 months
5. 1 day, 8 h

6. 2 cm, 4 mm
7. 2 years, 8 months
8. 3 h, 20 min
9. 6 m, 200 cm
10. £3, 25 p

Exercise 5

1. Draw a straight line half the length of these lines:

   (a) ─────────────────────────

   (b) ──────────────────────────────────

2. Draw a straight line one-quarter the length of this given line:

   ──────────────────────────────

3. Draw a straight line one-fifth the length of this line:

   ────────────────────────────────────

4. Draw a straight line one-third the length of these lines:

   (a) ──────────────────────────────

   (b)

   ────────────────────────────────────

Exercise 6

What fraction of the second quantity is the first?

e.g. £2, £6

£2 is $\dfrac{2}{6}$ of £6; that is, $\dfrac{1}{3}$ of £6.

1. £3, £12

2. £4, £12

3. 5 min, 15 min

4. 2 km, 16 km

5. 4 years, 20 years

6. 10 h, 15 h

7. £2, £10

8. £6, £10

9. 9 km, 12 km

10. 9 m, 24 m

11. 10 cm, 16 cm

12. 4 months, 1 year

13. 6 months, 3 years

14. 50 p, £2

15. 40 p, £2

16. 40 min, 2 h

Exercise 7

1. Here is a recipe to make 'Brown stew':

Ingredients
700 g ($1\frac{1}{2}$ lb) stewing steak
30 ml (2 tbsps) fat or oil
2 onions, skinned and sliced
2 carrots, pared and sliced
100 g (4 levels tbsps) flour
900 ml ($1\frac{1}{2}$ pt) stock
salt and pepper
bouquet garni

Cut the meat into 1 cm ($\frac{1}{2}$ in) cubes. Heat the fat or oil in a frying pan and fry the onions and carrots until browned. Remove from the pan and fry the meat until browned. Put the meat and vegetables in a casserole. Add the flour to the fat remaining in the pan, stir well and add the stock gradually; bring to the boil, season and add to the casserole, with the bouquet garni. Cover and cook in the oven at 170 °C (325 °F) Mark 3 for about 2 h.

Remove the bouquet garni before serving.

The recipe above is for four people. Copy the list of ingredients but give them for
(a) 2 people,
(b) 8 people.

2. Here is a recipe to make 'Coffee walnut fudge':

Ingredients
700 g ($1\frac{1}{2}$ lb) granulated sugar

300 mℓ ($\frac{1}{2}$ pt) evaporated milk

150 mℓ ($\frac{1}{4}$ pt) water
100 g (4 oz) butter
25 mℓ ($1\frac{1}{2}$ level tbsps) instant coffee
50 g (2 oz) walnuts, chopped

Grease a tin 20.5 cm (8 in) square. Put the sugar, milk, water and butter into a 3.4 ℓ (6 pt) heavy-based saucepan. Blend the coffee with 15 mℓ (1 tbsp) water and add to the pan. Stir over a low heat until the sugar has dissolved. Boil gently to 116 °C (240 °F) (soft ball stage); stir to prevent sticking. Remove from the heat, place the pan on a cool surface, add the nuts and beat with a wooden spoon until thick, creamy and beginning to 'grain'. Pour into the tin and leave until nearly cold; mark into squares. When firm, cut with a sharp knife.

The recipe above is for 2 lb of coffee walnut fudge. Copy the list of ingredients but give them for
(a) 1 lb of fudge,
(b) 3 lb of fudge.

Exercise 8

1. A lorry travels at 35 m.p.h. A car travels twice as fast. How fast is the car travelling?

2. A bus travels at 45 m.p.h. A cyclist travels one-third the speed. How fast is the cyclist travelling?

3. Kath walks 8 km. Ken walks three times as far. How far does Ken walk?

4. Betty works for 12 h. Bill works for one-quarter of that time. For how long does Bill work?

5. Stan jogs for 45 min. Susan jogs for two-thirds of that time. For how long does Susan jog?

6. Linus swims 300 m. Diana swims five times as far. How many metres is that?

8 Scales and Scale Drawings

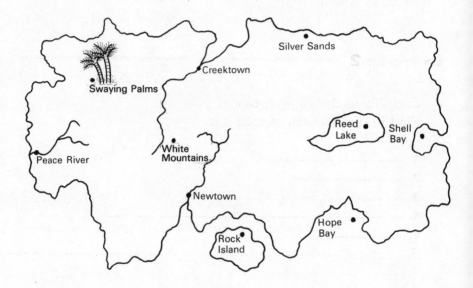

Scale: 1 cm to 1 km.

Look at the scale of the map above. Use it to find the distances, in kilometres, between the points marked:

1. Creektown to Silver Sands.

2. Peace River to Rock Island.

3. Silver Sands to Hope Bay.

4. Swaying Palms to Newtown.

5. White Mountains to Newtown.

6. Rock Island to Shell Bay.

7. Reed Lake to Peace River.

8. Silver Sands to White Mountains.

9. Swaying Palms to Reed Lake.

10. Peace River to Silver Sands.

11. Hope Bay to Rock Island.

12. Newtown to Shell Bay.

Exercise 2

Each line is drawn to a scale of 1 cm to 2 m.
Find the true length of each line.

1. ─────────────
2. ──────────
3. ────────────────────
4. ──────────────────────────
5. ──────
6. ───────────────────────────────────
7. ───────────
8. ──────────────────

Exercise 3

Each line is drawn to a scale of 1 cm to 3 km.
Find the true length of each line.

1. ──────
2. ────────────
3. ───────────────────────
4. ──────────────────
5. ────────────────────────

Exercise 4

Each line is drawn to a scale of 1 cm to 5 m.
Find the true length of each line.

1. ─────────
2. ──────────────────
3. ───────────────
4. ─────────────────────
5. ────────────────────────

Exercise 5

Each line is drawn to a scale of 1 cm to 4 km.
Find the true length of each line.

1. ────────
2. ──────────────
3. ────────────────────
4. ───────
5. ─────────────

Exercise 6

1. The rectangle has been drawn to a scale of 1 cm to 1 m.

   (a) Find its true length.
   (b) Find its true breadth.
   (c) Find the true length of one of its diagonals.

2. The parallelogram has been drawn to a scale of 1 cm to 6 cm.
Find the true length of:
(*a*) diagonal AC,
(*b*) diagonal BD,
(*c*) side CD.

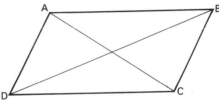

3. The diagram shows a ship, S, and two lighthouses, L_1 and L_2.
The scale is 1 cm to 2 km.

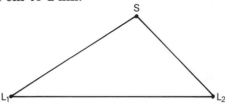

(*a*) How far is the ship from lighthouse L_1?
(*b*) How far is the ship from lighthouse L_2?
(*c*) What is the distance between the lighthouses?

4. A plan of a field is given.
The scale is 1 cm to 40 m.
Find:
(*a*) The length of each side
of the field.
(*b*) The perimeter of the field.

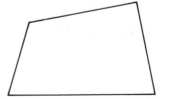

Exercise 7

Use a scale of 1 cm to 1 m to draw these lines:

1. 4 m	**3.** 6 m	**5.** 10 m	**7.** 15 m	**9.** 12.5 m
2. 9 m	**4.** 7 m	**6.** 2 m	**8.** 7.5 m	**10.** 4.5 m

Exercise 8

Use a scale of 1 cm to 2 km to draw these lines:

1. 8 km
2. 10 km
3. 20 km
4. 14 km
5. 24 km

6. 28 km
7. 5 km
8. 9 km
9. 17 km
10. 25 km

Exercise 9

Use a scale of 1 cm to 4 cm to draw these lines:

1. 12 cm
2. 20 cm
3. 32 cm
4. 40 cm
5. 28 cm

6. 16 cm
7. 48 cm
8. 14 cm
9. 22 cm
10. 38 cm

Exercise 10

Look carefully at this scale:

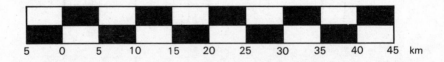

Use the scale to draw these lines:

1. 10 km
2. 20 km
3. 45 km
4. 55 km
5. 60 km

6. 5 km
7. 35 km
8. 25 km
9. 12.5 km
10. 17.5 km

Exercise 11

1. Here is the ground floor plan of a house.
It is drawn to a scale of 1 cm to 1 m.

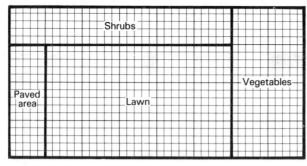

(a) Give the length and breadth of the lounge.

(b) Give the length and breadth of the dining room.

(c) Give the length and breadth of the kitchen.

(d) Find the area of the lounge.

2. Here is the plan of a garden.
Scale: 1 cm to 5 m.

(a) How long is the lawn?

(b) Give the length and breadth of the shrubbery?

(c) Find the length and breadth of the vegetable patch?

(d) Find the perimeter of the whole garden.

(e) What is the area of the paving?

Exercise 12

1. A rectangular room measures 6 m by 4 m. Make a scale drawing of the room. Use a scale of 1 cm to 1 m.

2. A rectangular playground is 50 m long and 30 m wide. Make a scale drawing. Use a scale of 1 cm to 10 m.

3. Make a scale drawing of a rectangular table top. The table top measures 2 m by 1 m. Use a scale of 1 cm to 50 cm (that is 1 cm to $\frac{1}{2}$ m).

4. A ship starts at A. It sails 12 km due East. It then turns South and sails 5 km due South until it reaches B.

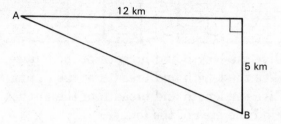

   Draw the journey using a scale of 1 cm to 1 km. Use your drawing to find the direct distance from A to B. (Note that the given sketch is not accurately drawn.)

5. Make a scale drawing from the given sketch.
   Use a scale of 1 cm to 10 m.
   Find the height of the tower.

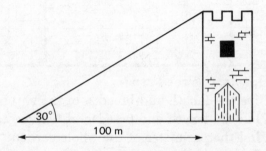

9 Bases

A For each question, copy the crosses.
Draw round groups of eight.

e.g.

1.

4.

2.

5.

3.

6.

7.

8.

B Make a table of your results:

	Number of crosses	Number of groups of eight	Number of crosses left over
e.g.	30	3	6
1.	21		
2.			
3.			
4.			
5.			
6.			

Exercise 2 ▬▬▬▬▬▬▬▬▬▬▬▬▬▬▬▬▬▬▬▬ **M**

A For each question, copy the crosses.
Draw round groups of five.

e.g.

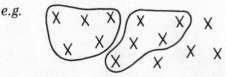

1.

2.

3. X X X X
X X X X X
X X X X
X X

6. X X X
X X X
X X

4. X X X X X
X X X X X
X X X X X
X X X X

7. X X X X X
X X X X
X X X X X
X X X X X X

5. X X X X
X X X X X X
X X X X X
X X X X X

8. X X X X
X X X X X
X X X X
X X X X

B Make a table of your results:

	Number of crosses	Number of groups of five	Number of crosses left over
e.g.	14	2	4
1.			
2.			
3.			
4.			
5.			
6.			
7.			
8.			

Exercise 3

Copy the following.

Write the correct number in place of each question mark.

e.g. 1 $65_8 = 6$ eights $+ 5$ units $= 48 + 5 = 53_{ten}$

e.g. 2 $32_5 = 3$ fives $+ 2$ units $= 15 + 2 = 17_{ten}$

1. $31_6 = \boxed{?}$ sixes $+ \boxed{?}$ unit $= \boxed{?} + \boxed{?} = \boxed{?}_{ten}$

2. $14_7 = \boxed{?}$ seven $+ \boxed{?}$ units $= \boxed{?} + \boxed{?} = \boxed{?}_{ten}$

3. $22_4 = \boxed{?}$ fours $+ \boxed{?}$ units $= \boxed{?} + \boxed{?} = \boxed{?}_{ten}$

4. $21_3 = \boxed{?}$ threes $+ \boxed{?}$ unit $= \boxed{?} + \boxed{?} = \boxed{?}_{ten}$

5. $53_6 = \boxed{?}$ sixes $+ \boxed{?}$ units $= \boxed{?} + \boxed{?} = \boxed{?}_{ten}$

6. $35_8 = \boxed{?}$ eights $+ \boxed{?}$ units $= \boxed{?} + \boxed{?} = \boxed{?}_{ten}$

7. $72_9 = \boxed{?}$ nines $+ \boxed{?}$ units $= \boxed{?} + \boxed{?} = \boxed{?}_{ten}$

8. $40_5 = \boxed{?}$ fives $+ \boxed{?}$ units $= \boxed{?} + \boxed{?} = \boxed{?}_{ten}$

Exercise 4

A Tins of soup are put into boxes of eight.

1. How many tins are there in 3 boxes?

2. How many tins are there in 7 boxes?

3. How many tins are there if there are 4 boxes and 2 tins left over?

4. How many tins are there if there are 2 boxes and 6 tins left over?

5. How many tins are there if there are 3 boxes and 7 tins left over?

6. How many tins are there if there is 1 box and 5 tins left over?

B Write these base 8 (octal) numbers in base ten (denary):

1. 30_8 **3.** 42_8 **5.** 37_8

2. 70_8 **4.** 26_8 **6.** 15_8

C Write what you notice about your answers in parts A and B.

Exercise 5

Write these base 8 numbers in base ten:

1. 14_8 **5.** 41_8 **9.** 33_8 **13.** 57_8

2. 16_8 **6.** 53_8 **10.** 40_8 **14.** 45_8

3. 24_8 **7.** 25_8 **11.** 50_8 **15.** 77_8

4. 27_8 **8.** 66_8 **12.** 73_8

Exercise 6

Tins of soup are put into boxes of eight.

1. Write how many boxes are needed to hold:
   (a) 48 tins   (b) 32 tins?

2. How many boxes are needed and how many tins are left over if I have:

   (a) 19 tins   (e) 41 tins   (i) 55 tins

   (b) 10 tins   (f) 39 tins   (j) 60 tins

   (c) 25 tins   (g) 50 tins   (k) 46 tins

   (d) 36 tins   (h) 17 tins   (l) 57 tins

10 Time, Timetables and the Calendar

For thousands of years, the Sun, Moon and stars have been used as timekeepers. The Earth orbits the Sun in a year. The time from one new moon to the next gives a month. The rotation of the Earth on its axis shows how the days pass.

The days were divided into hours, and through the ages, many devices were invented to give the time of day. Some of these devices are shown here:

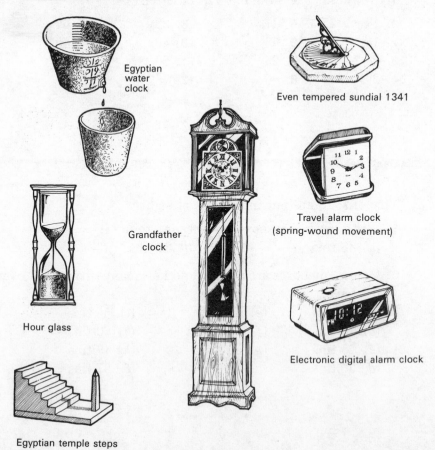

Egyptian water clock

Even tempered sundial 1341

Hour glass

Grandfather clock

Travel alarm clock (spring-wound movement)

Electronic digital alarm clock

Egyptian temple steps

Exercise 1

1. Here are the days of the week.
   The order is jumbled.
   Write them underneath each other in the correct order.
   Start with Sunday.

   Sunday
   Wednesday
   Friday
   Tuesday
   Thursday
   Monday
   Saturday

2. Here are the abbreviations for the days of the week.
   Write each abbreviation next to its correct full name.

   Sun
   Mon
   Sat
   Wed
   Thurs
   Tues
   Fri

3. How many days are there in:
   (*a*) 2 weeks?   (*b*) 5 weeks?   (*c*) 9 weeks?

4. How many weeks are there in:
   (*a*) 21 days?   (*b*) 49 days?   (*c*) 56 days?

5. How many days are there in:
   (*a*) 13 weeks?   (*b*) 26 weeks?   (*c*) 52 weeks?

6. How many days are there in:
   (*a*) one week and four days?
   (*b*) two weeks and three days?
   (*c*) four weeks and one day?
   (*d*) three weeks and six days?

7. There are 24 h in 1 day. How many hours are there in:
   (*a*) 2 days?
   (*b*) 3 days?
   (*c*) 10 days?
   (*d*) 1 week?

Exercise 2

A Copy and complete:

1. One hour   = $\boxed{?}$ min   9. Three hours = $\boxed{?}$ min

2. Two hours   = $\boxed{?}$ min   10. 1 h 40 min   = $\boxed{?}$ min

3. 5 h   = $\boxed{?}$ min   11. 2 h 10 min   = $\boxed{?}$ min

4. Half an hour = $\boxed{?}$ min   12. 2 h 25 min   = $\boxed{?}$ min

5. $\frac{1}{4}$ of an hour = $\boxed{?}$ min   13. 3 h 15 min   = $\boxed{?}$ min

6. $\frac{3}{4}$ of an hour = $\boxed{?}$ min   14. 5 h 20 min   = $\boxed{?}$ min

7. $1\frac{1}{2}$ h   = $\boxed{?}$ min   15. 1 h 18 min   = $\boxed{?}$ min

8. Four hours   = $\boxed{?}$ min   16. 2 h 34 min   = $\boxed{?}$ min

B Write in hours and minutes:

1. 80 min   6. 170 min   11. 135 min
2. 110 min   7. 230 min   12. 215 min
3. 150 min   8. 75 min   13. 132 min
4. 200 min   9. 105 min   14. 144 min
5. 70 min   10. 145 min   15. 83 min

Exercise 3

A Copy and complete:

1. One minute   = $\boxed{?}$ s   6. 1 min 20 s = $\boxed{?}$ s

2. Three minutes = $\boxed{?}$ s   7. $1\frac{3}{4}$ min   = $\boxed{?}$ s

3. 4 min   = $\boxed{?}$ s   8. 2 min 15 s = $\boxed{?}$ s

4. 6 min   = $\boxed{?}$ s   9. 1 min 24 s = $\boxed{?}$ s

5. $2\frac{1}{2}$ min   = $\boxed{?}$ s   10. 3 min 45 s = $\boxed{?}$ s

B Write in minutes and seconds:

1. 100 s	**5.** 120 s	**9.** 145 s
2. 140 s	**6.** 300 s	**10.** 165 s
3. 75 s	**7.** 115 s	**11.** 400 s
4. 90 s	**8.** 205 s	**12.** 153 s

Exercise 4

1. A timer needs to be set for 1 h 35 min. How many minutes is that?

2. A runner ran 4 laps of a track at 68 s per lap. What was his time in minutes and seconds?

3. Four women ran a 4 × 800 m relay. Their times were 2 min 3 s, 2 min 8 s, 2 min 5 s and 2 min 4 s. What was the total time taken?

4. Change 1 h into seconds.

5. Change 2 h into seconds.

Exercise 5

A How long is a minute?
Try this:
With a friend's help, try to estimate 1 minute.
Your friend should use a stopwatch or an ordinary watch that shows seconds. When he or she tells you to start, try to estimate 1 minute. Tell your friend when you think exactly 1 minute has passed. Note the actual time measured. By how many seconds were you wrong?
Now time your friend.

B Use a stopwatch to help you to find the number of beats your pulse makes in 30 s. (It may be easier if a friend helps you.) How many beats would that be per minute?

1. Type the following program into a computer (it should work on most computers):

```
10   REM ***TIMING***
20   LET I = 0
30   PRINT "START"
40   FOR N = 1 TO 100
50   LET I = I + 1
60   NEXT N
70   PRINT "STOP"
80   END
```

2. Have a stopwatch ready and run the program. When START is printed, start the stopwatch. When STOP is printed, stop the stopwatch. Note the time taken for the program to run.

3. Change line 40 of the program as follows then repeat step 2 above:
   (a) 40   FOR N = 1 TO 500
   (b) 40   FOR N = 1 TO 1000
   (c) 40   FOR N = 1 TO 5000
   (d) 40   FOR N = 1 TO 10000
   (e) 40   FOR N = 1 TO 50000

4. What is the program making the computer do after printing START and before printing STOP?

5. Compare the times you have noted.
   (a) Is the time for 10000 (in line 40, question 3(d)) double the time for 5000 (in 3(c))?
   (b) Is the time for 50000 five times the time for 10000?

6. If possible, run the program on different makes of computer. Find out which computer is fastest in running this program.

Exercise 7

How far away is a storm?
Read this:
Light travels faster than sound.

Light travels about 186 000 miles in one second. Sound travels about 1 mile in 5 s.

When you see the lightning, count the seconds until you hear the thunder.

If you count 5 s the storm is 1 mile away;
                    10 s the storm is 2 miles away;
                    15 s the storm is 3 miles away; and so on.

Or, in kilometres,

if you count 3 s the storm is about 1 km away;
                  6 s the storm is about 2 km away;
                  9 s the storm is about 3 km away; and so on.

Try the above during the next storm.

Exercise 8   M

1. Copy the tally chart:

Time	Tally	Frequency
20.00		
20.30		
21.00		
21.30		
22.00		
22.30		
23.00		
23.30		
24.00		

2. Carry out a survey of the bedtimes of pupils in your class. Complete the tally chart. Pupils should give last night's bedtime and should give the nearest 'o'clock' or 'half-past' time as on the tally chart.

3. Draw a bar chart to show your results.

4. Write a sentence about bedtimes of pupils in your class. (Your graph should help you to think of one.)

Exercise 9 ════════════════════════════ M

There are 24 hours in a day.
Times throughout a day can be shown on a time line.

1. Copy the following time line:

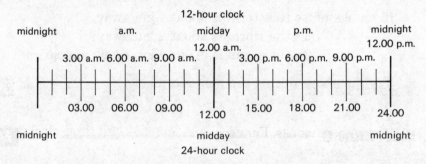

2. Copy and complete the table. (The time line may help you.)

12-hour clock	24-hour clock
3.00 a.m. =	
5.00 a.m. =	
=	07.00 h
8.30 a.m. =	
=	09.30 h
11.30 a.m. =	
12.00 a.m. =	

128

12-hour clock	24-hour clock
1.00 p.m. =	
=	14.00 h
5.30 p.m. =	
7.00 p.m. =	
=	19.30 h
=	21.00 h
10.30 p.m. =	
=	23.30 h

Exercise 10   M

Copy these clocks. For each question make all three clocks show
the same time.

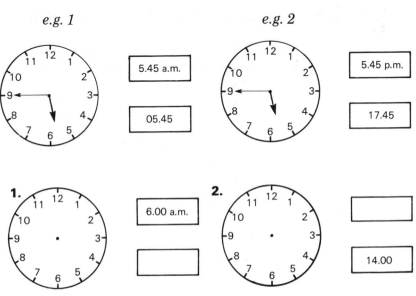

e.g. 1

5.45 a.m.

05.45

e.g. 2

5.45 p.m.

17.45

1.

6.00 a.m.

2.

14.00

3.

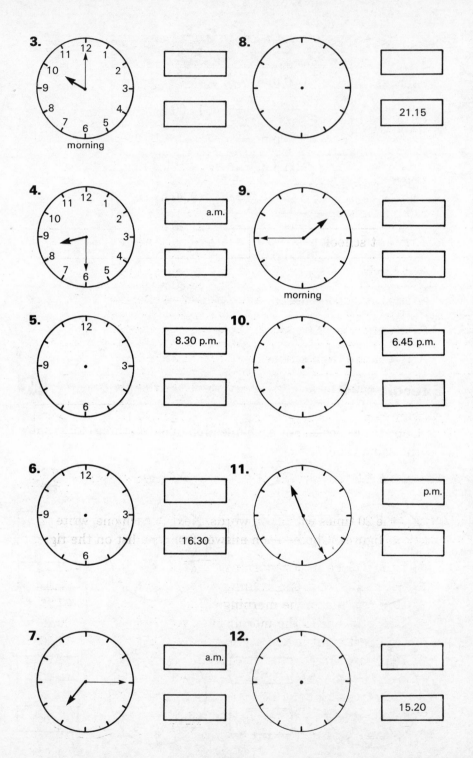

morning

8.

21.15

4.

a.m.

9.

morning

5.

8.30 p.m.

10.

6.45 p.m.

6.

16.30

11.

p.m.

7.

a.m.

12.

15.20

Exercise 11 M

Copy this table. Complete it for a school day.

Daily timetable	12-hour clock	24-hour clock
Get out of bed		
Have breakfast		
Set off for school		
Arrive at school		
Eat lunch		
Afternoon school starts		
Afternoon school finished		
Arrive home from school		
Have evening meal		
Go to bed		

Exercise 12 M

Copy the 20 times written in words. Next to each one, write the time in figures. Choose each answer from the list on the right.

1. Nine o'clock in the morning		21.10
2. Seven o'clock in the evening		03.15
3. Half past six in the morning		07.25
4. Half past one in the morning		00.20
5. Half past eight in the evening		14.10
6. Half past three in the afternoon		16.15
7. Quarter past three in the morning		09.00
8. Twenty past five in the morning		01.30
9. Five past eleven in the morning		11.05
10. Quarter past four in the evening		19.00

11.	Ten past nine in the evening	20.30
12.	Twenty past eleven in the evening	00.15
13.	Twenty-five past seven in the morning	12.15
14.	Five past ten in the evening	06.30
15.	Five past ten in the morning	22.05
16.	Ten past two in the morning	23.20
17.	Ten past two in the afternoon	15.30
18.	Quarter past twelve in the afternoon	05.20
19.	Twenty past twelve, midnight	02.10
20.	Quarter past twelve in the morning	10.05

Exercise 13 ===================================== **M**

Copy the 15 times written in words. Next to each one, write the time in figures. Choose each answer from the list on the right.

1.	Quarter to eight in the morning	09.40
2.	Quarter to six in the morning	20.40
3.	Quarter to six in the evening	04.45
4.	Twenty to ten in the morning	12.55
5.	Ten to seven in the evening	07.45
6.	Five to three in the morning	17.45
7.	Five to three in the afternoon	16.35
8.	Twenty to nine in the evening	23.35
9.	Twenty-five to five in the evening	11.35
10.	Ten to eleven in the evening	05.45
11.	Ten to eleven in the morning	10.50
12.	Quarter to five in the morning	14.55
13.	Twenty-five to twelve in the morning	18.50
14.	Twenty-five to twelve in the evening	22.50
15.	Five to one in the afternoon	02.55

Exercise 14 =====================================

Write how many minutes there are up to the next hour, if the time is now:

1. 09.50	**3.** 12.55	**5.** 06.35
2. 11.45	**4.** 02.40	**6.** 15.45

7. 07.52	12. 21.20	17. 22.18
8. 05.49	13. 01.25	18. 18.12
9. 14.41	14. 10.15	19. 04.23
10. 19.38	15. 23.05	20. 20.07
11. 16.30	16. 03.27	

Exercise 15

1. I got to the bus stop 25 min early. After 10 min had gone by, how much longer had I to wait for the bus?

2. Pat had three tasks to complete in one hour. It took her 15 min to wash up and 20 min to tidy her bedroom. How much time was left?

3. Ron arrived at school fifteen minutes early. If school started at 08.55, at what time did he arrive?

4. The train was due at 14.25. If it was ten minutes late, at what time did it arrive?

5. Jean caught the bus at 07.45. Her bus journey took 25 min. At what time did she get off the bus?

6. I had to go to a friend's house at 20.15. If I was 35 min late, at what time did I get there?

7. Stephen was on the bus for 1 h 20 min. He then walked the rest of his journey. If he walked for 12 min, how long was his journey altogether?

8. Jota set off for home at 15.40. He walked for 15 min, had a 20 min bus journey then walked for a further 10 min. At what time did he get home?

Using a Timetable

Exercise 16

Here is a second year school timetable:

		Mon	Tues	Wed	Thurs	Fri
08.55						
09.20			Registration/Assembly			
09.55	1	History	Computer appreciation ↑	English	Maths	French
10.30	2	Geography		Geography	Music	PE
10.45						
11.25	3	Domestic science/ Needlework ↑	RE	CDT ↕	RE	Physics ↕
12.00	4		French		French	
13.10				Lunch		
13.15				Registration		
13.50	5	Maths ↑	English ↑	French	English ↕	Chemistry ↕
14.25	6			Maths		
14.35						
15.10	7	French	Maths	Biology ↕	Games ↕	Art ↕
15.45	8	English	History			

Use the timetable to answer these questions:

1. On which day is music?

2. On which day is the first geography lesson?

3. At what time does the second history lesson start?

4. How long does the PE lesson last?

5. How long is the computer lesson?

6. How long is the CDT (craft, design and technology) lesson?

7. How long is the lunch break?

8. Which is the longest science lesson, biology, chemistry or physics?

9. Find the total weekly time for English.

10. Find the total weekly time for maths.

11. The games lesson finished ten minutes early so that the pupils could get changed before the school finished. At what time did the lesson finish?

12. Stivo went to the doctor's on Thursday morning and was two hours late for school. Which lesson did he go to when he got to school?

13. Caragh arrived at school half an hour before school started. At what time did she arrive?

14. Henry arrived at school twenty minutes before school started. At what time did he arrive?

15. I set off for school at ten to eight in the morning. I waited quarter of an hour for the bus. The bus journey was 20 min. I then had a 10-min walk to school. At what time did I arrive at school?

Reading a Timetable

Here is a timetable. It shows the times of some trains between London and Manchester.

London (Euston) → Manchester (Piccadilly)

London (Euston)	08.15	11.50	15.50	18.10
Stoke-on-Trent	10.11	13.47	17.41	20.50
Macclesfield	10.32	14.07	18.03	21.10
Stockport	10.48	14.27	18.21	21.27
Manchester (Piccadilly)	10.57	14.35	18.30	21.35

Manchester (Piccadilly) → London (Euston)

Manchester (Piccadilly)	07.00	10.15	15.35	19.15
Stockport	07.08	10.23	15.43	19.24
Macclesfield	07.22	10.37	15.57	19.38
Stoke-on-Trent	07.42	10.57	16.17	19.58
London (Euston)	09.35	12.58	18.20	21.55

Exercise 17

Use the timetable above.

1. If you catch the 11.50 train from London (Euston), at what time would you arrive in Stockport?

2. At what time does the 18.10 train from London (Euston) arrive at Manchester (Piccadilly)?

3. At what time does the 15.35 train from Manchester (Piccadilly) arrive at London (Euston)?

4. At what time does the 19.38 train from Macclesfield arrive at London (Euston)?

5. Tom leaves Stoke-on-Trent on the 17.41 train. At what time does he arrive in Stockport?

6. Silvia travelled from London (Euston) to Manchester (Piccadilly). If she arrived in Manchester at 10.57, which train did she catch from London (Euston)?

7. Liz travelled from Macclesfield to London (Euston). If she arrived in London at 12.58, at what time did she leave Macclesfield?

8. Paul arrived in Stoke-on-Trent at 16.17. At what time did he leave Stockport?

9. A train arrived in Stoke-on-Trent at 07.42. At what time did it leave Stockport?

10. If you wish to arrive in Manchester at 18.30, at what time must you leave Macclesfield?

11. How long does it take to travel from Stockport to Stoke-on-Trent on the 10.23 train?

12. How long does the fastest train take to get from Macclesfield to Stockport?

Calendars

Exercise 18

Here are the months of the year.
They are given in the wrong order.
September, February, December, October, July, May, January, March, November, April, June, August.
Write them in the correct order.

To Find the Number of Days in Each Month

Method 1

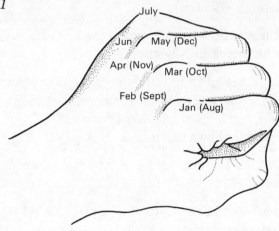

1. Clench your fist.

2. Label the knuckles and valleys with the months of the year as shown.

3. The months that are labelled at the knuckles each have 31 days. The other months have 30 days except February which has 28 days (in a leap year it has 29 days).

Method 2

Learn this: Thirty days hath September,
April, June and November.
All the rest have thirty-one
Except February alone,
Which has twenty-eight days clear
And twenty-nine in each leap year.

Exercise 19

1. Which is the eighth month of the year?

2. Which is the fourth month of the year?

3. How many days are there in October?

4. How many days are there in July?

5. Put these dates (all in the same year) in the correct order: 9 May, 23 March, 16 October, 11 January, 30 May, 23 April, 18 December, 1 September

Exercise 20 ═══════════════════════════ M

The calendar shows the month of August:

AUGUST						
Sun	Mon	Tues	Wed	Thurs	Fri	Sat
			1			4
5						
		14				
			29			

1. Copy and complete the calendar.

2. On what day will 1 September of the same year fall?

3. What will be the date of the second Wednesday in September?

4. How many Saturdays will there be in September?

5. List the dates of all the Mondays in September.

Exercise 21

1. If the first day of a month is a Friday, write the days for these dates:

(*a*) 6th   (*b*) 18th   (*c*) 25th   (*d*) 10th   (*e*) 27th

2. If the first day of a month is a Tuesday, write the days for these dates:

(*a*) 8th   (*b*) 11th   (*c*) 15th   (*d*) 21st   (*e*) 30th

3. If 12 June was a Thursday, write the dates of all the Thursdays in June.

4. If 18 May was a Sunday, write the dates of all the Sundays in May.

5. If 30 October was a Tuesday, write the dates of all the Tuesdays in October.

Exercise 22

16 February 1979 can be written as 16.2.79.

A Write these dates using figures:

1. 23 June 1965   **6.** 25 Dec 1977
2. 4 Sept 1973   **7.** 1 Jan 1981
3. 19 April 1958   **8.** 21 Nov 1978
4. 2 July 1971   **9.** 15 Feb 1980
5. 8 Oct 1984   **10.** 13 Aug 1983

B Write these dates using the name of the month:

1. 12.5.72.   **5.** 28.6.82.
2. 6.10.81.   **6.** 17.11.79.
3. 21.3.78.   **7.** 13.4.84.
4. 1.9.67.   **8.** 18.8.81.

Exercise 23

1. How many years were there from November 1975 to November 1984?

2. Jim was born in March 1976. Pat was four years older. In what year was Pat born?

3. Susan was born in September 1971. Alan was born in September 1978.
(*a*) Who was younger?   (*b*) By how many years?

4. Kate was born in 1969. Henry was seven years younger. In what year was Henry born?

5. Steven was eight years old on 14 Oct 1984. When was he born?

6. Karen was twelve years old on 26.3.81. When was she born?

Exercise 24

There is only one day from 7 Aug to 8 Aug of the same year. (In counting from 7 to 8 you only count one!)

e.g. 1   The number of days from 7 Aug to 15 Aug = $\underline{8}$

e.g. 2   The number of days from 18 Dec to the 14 Jan = $\underline{27}$

Find the number of days from:
1. 2 June to 9 June
2. 11 Nov to 24 Nov
3. 4 Feb to 27 Feb
4. 21 May to 6 June
5. 26 Sept to 4 Oct
6. 15 Apr to 10 May
7. 17 Jan to 12 Feb
8. 20 July to 20 Aug
9. 12 Feb to 8 March in a leap year
10. 19 Feb to 6 March (not a leap year)

Copy and complete the table of holiday dates:

	Date of departure	Date of return	Number of nights
e.g. 1	15 Aug	22 Aug	7
e.g. 2	27 July	6 Aug	10
1.	4 Aug	15 Aug	
2.	2 Apr	17 Apr	
3.	9 Jan		12
4.	12 June		8
5.		21 Oct	5
6.	30 May	5 June	
7.	26 Dec		10
8.	28 Oct		15
9.		9 Apr	11
10.	14 Nov	4 Dec	
11.		11 Feb	21
12.	24 Sept		16

11 Area

Exercise 1

How many squares are there in each of these rectangles?

1.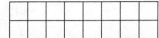

3.

2.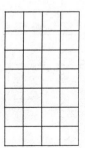

4.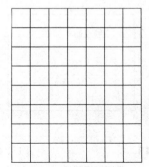

Exercise 2

Calculate the area of each rectangle:

1.

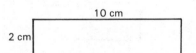

10 cm

2 cm

2.

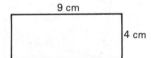

9 cm

4 cm

143

3.

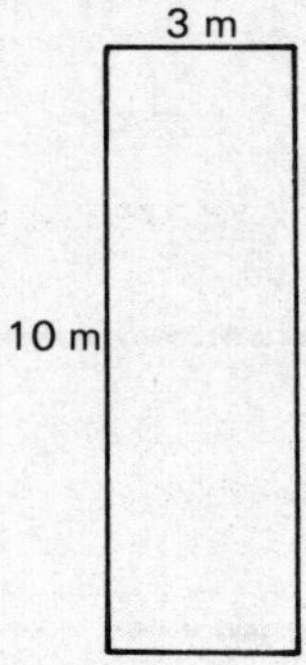

3 m

10 m

8.

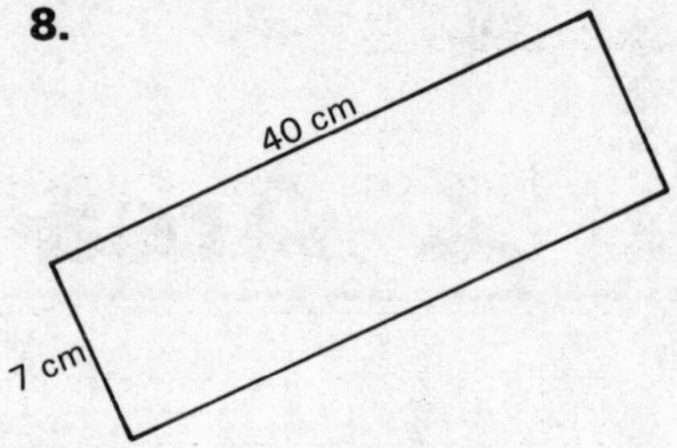

40 cm

7 cm

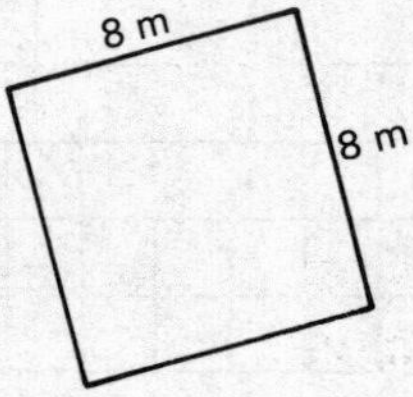

4.

8 m

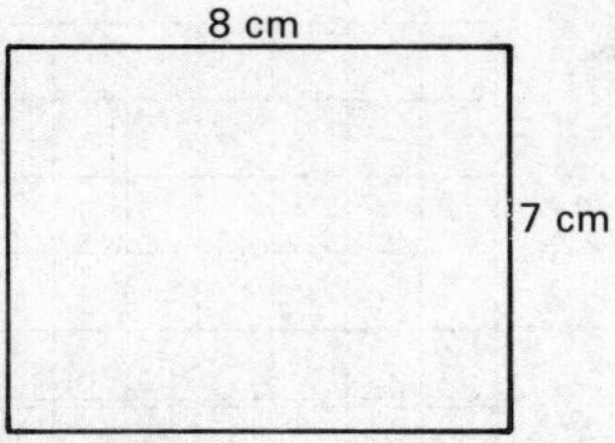

8 m

9.

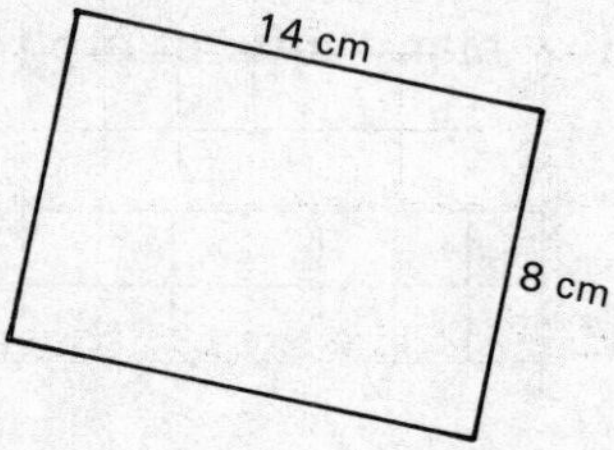

14 cm

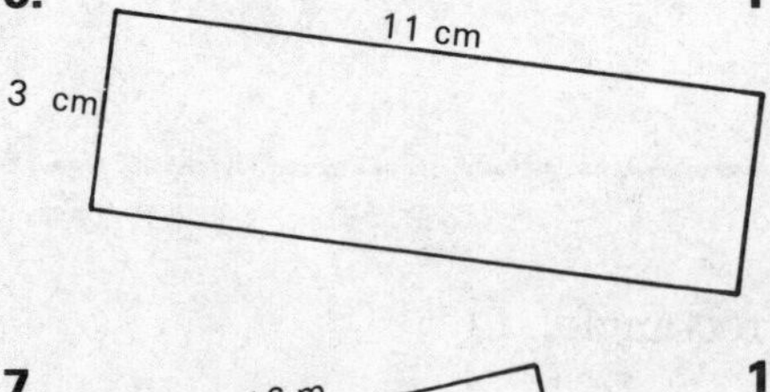

8 cm

5.

8 cm

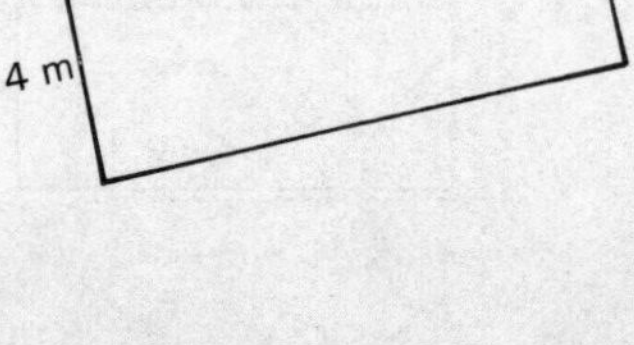

7 cm

10.

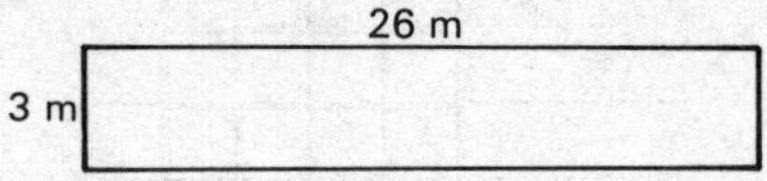

26 m

3 m

6.

11 cm

3 cm

11.

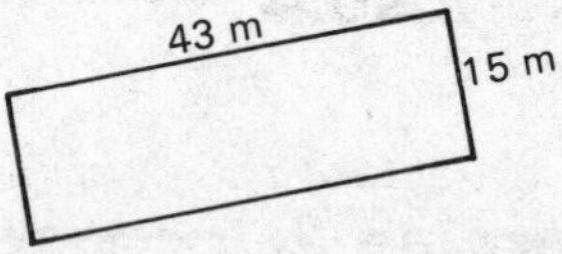

43 m

15 m

7.

16 m

4 m

12.

36 cm

13 cm

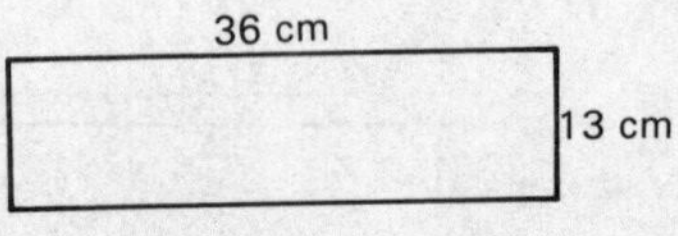

Exercise 3

1. Find the area of the rectangle in the middle:

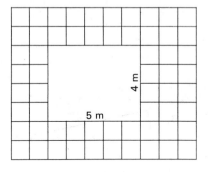

4 m

5 m

2. Find the area of this shape:

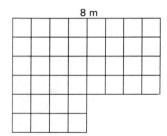

8 m

3. Find the area of the missing piece:

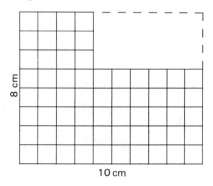

8 cm

10 cm

4. What is the area of this shape?

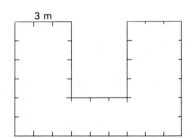

3 m

Exercise 4

A Calculate the area of each shape:

1.

12 cm

7 cm

2.

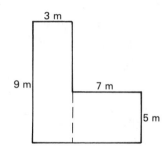

3 m

9 m

7 m

5 m

3.

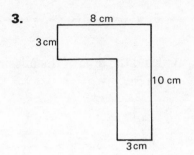

5.

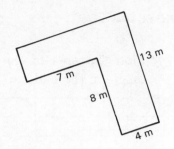

4.

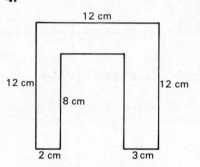

6.

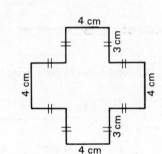

B Calculate the shaded areas:

1.

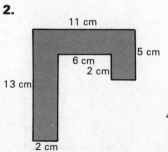

3.

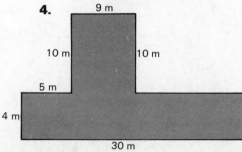

2.

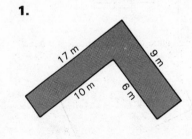

4.

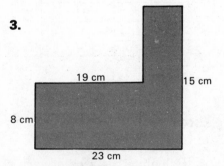

5.

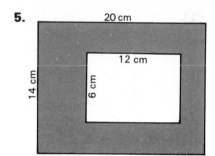
20 cm
12 cm
14 cm
6 cm

Exercise 5

For each rectangle, find the length of the missing side:

1.

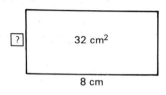
? 32 cm² 8 cm

4.

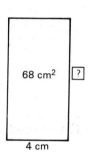
68 cm² ? 4 cm

2.

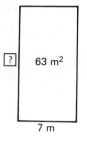
? 63 m² 7 m

5.

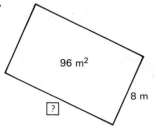
96 m² 8 m ?

3.

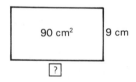
90 cm² 9 cm ?

6.

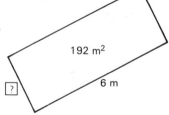
192 m² 6 m ?

147

7.

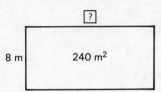

8 m   240 m²   ?

8.

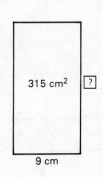

315 cm²   ?

9 cm

9.

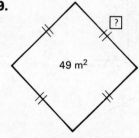

49 m²   ?

10.

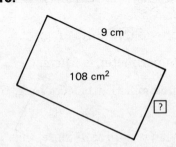

9 cm

108 cm²   ?

11.

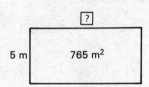

5 m   765 m²   ?

12.

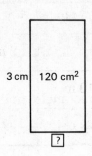

3 cm   120 cm²   ?

13.

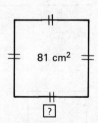

81 cm²   ?

14.

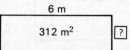

6 m

312 m²   ?

15.

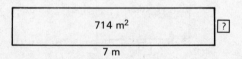

714 m²   ?

7 m

Copy and complete this table for the given rectangles:

	Length	Breadth	Area
1.	10 cm	5 cm	
2.	7 cm		21 cm²
3.		2 m	18 m²
4.	10 m		60 m²
5.	29 cm	10 cm	
6.		5 m	40 m²
7.		6 cm	72 cm²
8.	7 cm		91 cm²
9.	34 m	7 m	
10.	25 cm		100 cm²

Exercise 7

1. A room is 5 m long. If it is 3 m wide, find its area.

2. Find the area of a square if its perimeter is 24 cm.

3. A rectangle has a perimeter of 34 cm. If it is 9 cm long, find its area.

4. Some tiles are 15 cm square. How many of these tiles are needed to tile an area that is 90 cm by 75 cm?

5. Find the area of a rectangle with a perimeter of 36 cm if its breadth is 7 cm.

Surface Area

Exercise 8

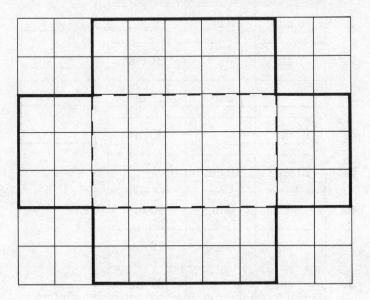

This shape can be used to make a box without a lid (and without flaps). You need to fold along the broken lines.

1. What would the length of the box be?

2. What would the breadth of the box be?

3. What would the height of the box be?

4. If this box was made from card, what area of card would be used?

5. On squared paper, draw the shape you would need to cut out to make another box without a lid, of length 7 cm, breadth 4 cm, and height 3 cm.
Such a shape is called a *net*.
The area found is the *surface area* of the box.

Exercise 9

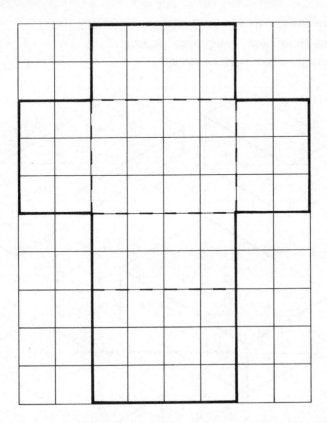

This shape is the net of a box with a lid (called a closed box or a cuboid).

1. How long is the box?

2. What is the breadth of the box?

3. Write its height.

4. Find its surface area.

5. On squared paper, draw the net of a cuboid that measures 5 cm by 4 cm by 2 cm. (That is, the length is 5 cm, the breadth is 4 cm and the height is 2 cm.)

Exercise 10

Copy these cuboids on dotty paper (triangular).
Draw their nets on squared paper.
Calculate their surface areas.

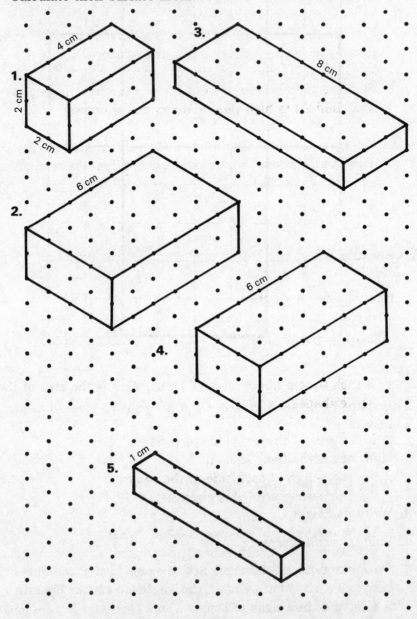

Exercise 11

1. A room is 5 m long, 4 m wide and 3 m high.
Calculate the area of one of the big walls.
Calculate the area of one of the small walls.
What is the area of the floor?
Find the total surface area (i.e. the area of all four walls + the floor + the ceiling (ignore doors and windows)).

2. Find the total surface area of a room that is 6 m long, 4 m wide, and 2.4 m high (ignore doors and windows).

3. Calculate the total area of the four walls of a room (ignore doors and windows) where the length is 7 m, the width 4 m and the height 2.5 m.

Exercise 12

Here is a net of a cube.

1. What fraction of the whole shape is one square?

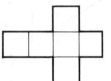

2. If each square has an area of 7 cm², what is the area of the whole shape?

3. If the area of the whole shape is 54 cm², find:
   (a) the area of one square,
   (b) the length of each side of the square,
   (c) the perimeter of this given net.

4. If the perimeter of this net is 56 cm, find:
   (a) the length of each side of one square,
   (b) the total area of the whole shape.

5. Carefully draw a net of a cube where each edge is 2 cm long.

Exercise 13

1. Find the area of a rectangle that is 4.6 cm long and 2 cm wide.

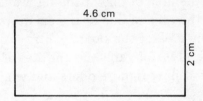

2. Find the area of a rectangle of length 8.3 cm and breadth 5 cm.

3. A rectangle measures 8 m by 5.4 m. Find its area.

4. A rectangular room is 4 m long and 3.9 m wide. Calculate its floor area.

5. A cardboard box without a lid is 7 cm long, 4 cm wide and 3.7 cm deep.

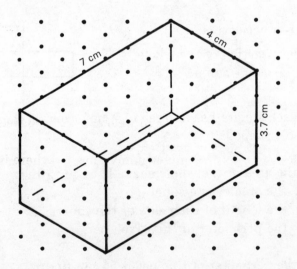

Draw its net.
Find the area of cardboard used to make the box (ignore any flaps).

Exercise 14

Find the area of each of these shapes:

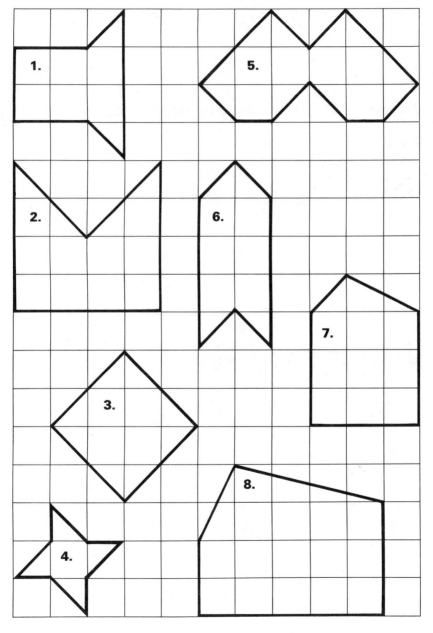

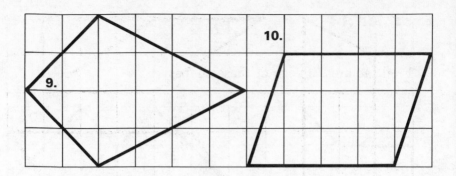

Areas of Parallelograms and Triangles

Exercise 15

Find the area of each parallelogram:

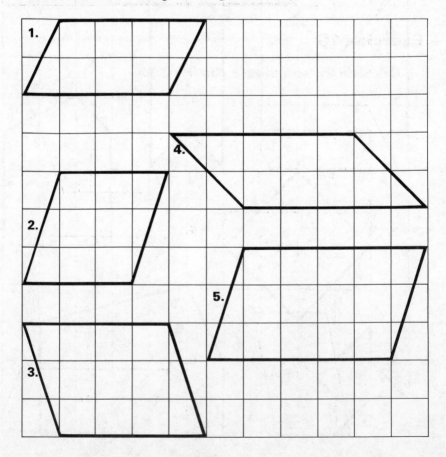

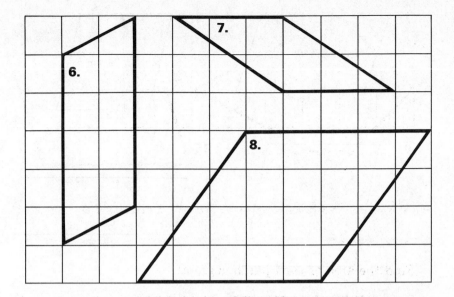

Exercise 16

Calculate the area of each parallelogram:

1.

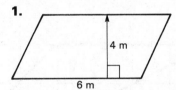

4 m

6 m

4.

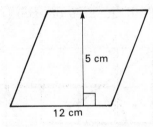

5 cm

12 cm

2.

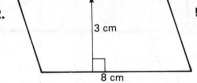

3 cm

8 cm

5.

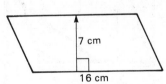

7 cm

16 cm

3.

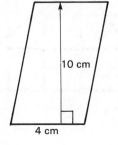

10 cm

4 cm

6.

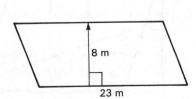

8 m

23 m

7.

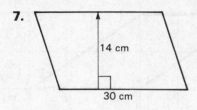

14 cm

30 cm

9.

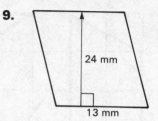

24 mm

13 mm

8.

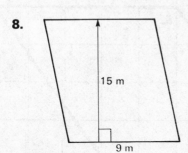

15 m

9 m

10.

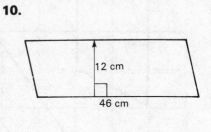

12 cm

46 cm

Exercise 17

Find the area of each triangle:

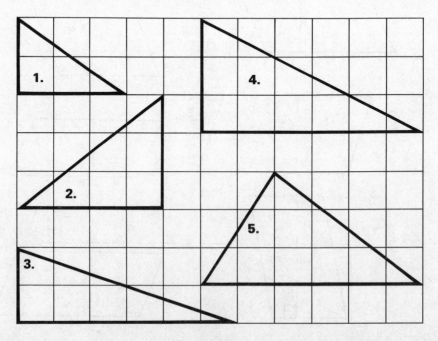

1.

4.

2.

5.

3.

158

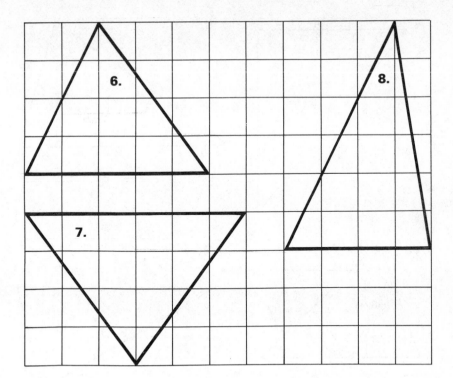

Exercise 18

Calculate the area of each triangle:

1.

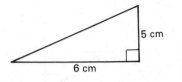

5 cm

6 cm

2.

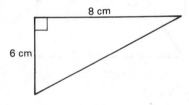

8 cm

6 cm

3.

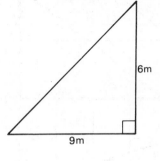

6m

9m

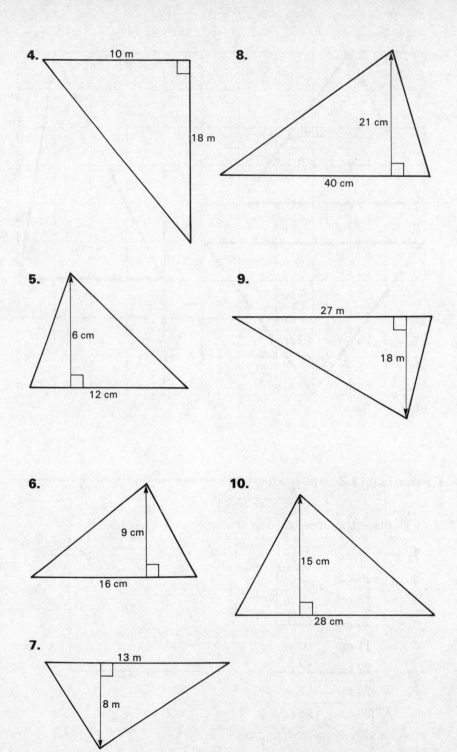

4. 10 m 18 m

8. 21 cm 40 cm

5. 6 cm 12 cm

9. 27 m 18 m

6. 9 cm 16 cm

10. 15 cm 28 cm

7. 13 m 8 m

Exercise 19

Calculate the areas of the parallelograms and triangles:

A

	Parallelograms	
	Base	Perpendicular height
1.	7 cm	6 cm
2.	9 cm	5 cm
3.	10 m	7 m
4.	14 m	6 m
5.	8 cm	15 cm
6.	17 cm	4 cm
7.	28 cm	9 cm
8.	21 m	14 m
9.	80 mm	60 mm
10.	54 cm	32 cm

B

	Triangles	
	Base	Perpendicular height
1.	8 cm	4 cm
2.	9 m	7 m
3.	12 cm	9 cm
4.	18 m	6 m
5.	20 cm	5 cm
6.	11 cm	10 cm
7.	22 m	16 m
8.	24 m	17 m
9.	30 cm	28 cm
10.	32 cm	26 cm

12 Percentages

This square has been divided into 100 equal parts.

Each small square is $\frac{1}{100}$ of the large square.

7 small squares have been shaded ($\frac{7}{100}$ have been shaded).

$\frac{7}{100}$ can be written as 7% (read as 7 per cent).

7 per cent means 7 out of 100 (that is $\frac{7}{100}$).

Exercise 1 ▬▬▬▬▬▬▬▬▬▬▬▬ **M**

Copy and complete the table on p. 163 for the following squares. (The first one has been done for you.)

1.

3.

5.

2.

4.

6.

7.

9.

8.

10.

	Fraction shaded	Percentage shaded			Fraction shaded	Percentage shaded
1.	$\frac{10}{100} = \frac{1}{10}$	10%	**6.**			
2.			**7.**			
3.			**8.**			
4.			**9.**			
5.			**10.**			

Exercise 2   **M**

On squared paper, using a 10 by 10 square for each question, shade the given percentages:

1. 80%

2. 30%

3. 55%

4. 85%

5. 65%

6. 44%

7. 32%

8. 24%

9. 76%

10. 91%

Exercise 3

Write as percentages:

e.g. 1 45 out of 100 = <u>45%</u>   *e.g. 2* $\frac{61}{100}$ = <u>61%</u>

1. 12 out of 100

2. 30 out of 100

3. 5 out of 100

4. 25 out of 100

5. 75 out of 100

6. 1 out of 100

7. 100 out of 100

8. 60 out of 100

9. 82 out of 100

10. 39 out of 100

11. $\frac{87}{100}$

12. $\frac{65}{100}$

13. $\frac{18}{100}$

14. $\frac{99}{100}$

15. $\frac{80}{100}$

16. $\frac{35}{100}$

17. $\frac{47}{100}$

18. $\frac{28}{100}$

19. $\frac{95}{100}$

20. $\frac{53}{100}$

Exercise 4

Write each percentage as a common fraction:

1. 37%

2. 51%

3. 79%

4. 23%

5. 89%

6. 13%

7. 31%

8. 27%

9. 21%

10. 73%

11. 57%

12. 9%

13. 50%

14. 25%

15. 75%

Exercise 5

A Try this on a calculator:

Since 48% = $\frac{48}{100}$, key in: $\boxed{4}\ \boxed{8}\ \boxed{\div}\ \boxed{1}\ \boxed{0}\ \boxed{0}\ \boxed{=}$

The display shows 48% as a decimal.

Now try these on a calculator. Change each percentage to a decimal. (Look carefully at each answer.)

1. 25%   **2.** 56%   **3.** 83%   **4.** 97%   **5.** 4%

B Without using a calculator, change each percentage to a decimal:

1. 75%	**5.** 77%	**9.** 33%	**13.** 71%
2. 22%	**6.** 14%	**10.** 46%	**14.** 69%
3. 41%	**7.** 59%	**11.** 3%	**15.** 11%
4. 86%	**8.** 98%	**12.** 92%	

Exercise 6

Here are the results of a test:

L. Lowe 51%	A. Pain 25%	R. U. Brown 63%
B. Wise 78%	I. B. Jolly 42%	U. B. Close 50%
E. Venn 54%	M. T. Case 36%	E. B. Bright 45%
B. Long 52%	C. I. Dee 49%	U. R. Topp 19%
U. Kay 73%	I. M. Wright 60%	I. M. Short 47%

Write out this list in order, from first to last. Put the percentage mark next to each person's name.

Reminder

$50\% = \frac{1}{2}$ $25\% = \frac{1}{4}$ $75\% = \frac{3}{4}$

Exercise 7

Find:

1. 50% of £8	**11.** 75% of £28
2. 50% of £14	**12.** 75% of £2
3. 50% of £26	**13.** 50% of £19
4. 50% of £7	**14.** 75% of £6
5. 25% of £12	**15.** 50% of £25
6. 25% of £40	**16.** 25% of £30
7. 25% of £48	**17.** 25% of £5
8. 25% of £10	**18.** 50% of £17.50
9. 75% of £20	**19.** 50% of £48.50
10. 75% of £60	**20.** 75% of £18

Revision Exercises VII to XII

Revision Exercise VII

1. (*a*) Draw a straight line
   that is three times as
   long as this line: _____
   (*b*) Draw a straight line that is half the length of the line
   above.

2. Enlarge this rectangle.
   Make each side twice as
   long.

3. How many times as big is 36 s compared with 9 s?

4. How many times as big is £2.50 compared with 50 p?

5. What fraction of £16 is £4?

6. What fraction of £15 is £3?

7. What fraction of 1 min is 15 s?

8. What fraction of 2 years is 4 months?

9. Ben spends £18. Colin spends twice as much. How much
   does Colin spend?

10. Liz walked 9 km. Mary walked two-thirds that distance.
    How far did Mary walk?

Revision Exercise VIII

1. Find the true length of each line:
    (a) _____ Scale: 1 cm to 6 m

    (b) _____ Scale: 1 cm to 5 km

    (c) _____ Scale: 1 cm to 8 km

    (d) _____ Scale: 1 cm to 3 m

2. The rhombus has been drawn to a scale of 1 cm to 4 m.
    (a) Find the true length of its sides.
    (b) Find the true length of its long diagonal.
    (c) Find the true length of its short diagonal.

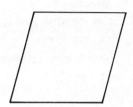

3. Use a scale of 1 cm to 1 km to drawn these lines:
    (a) 5 km   (b) 8.5 km

4. Use a scale of 1 cm to 2 m to draw these lines:
    (a) 12 m   (b) 15 m

5. Make a scale drawing of the playground shown. Use a scale of 1 cm to 5 m.
    From your scale drawing, find the true length of the missing side.

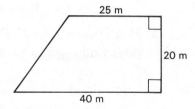

25 m

20 m

40 m

167

Revision Exercise IX

1. (a) Copy the crosses.
   (b) Draw round groups of eight.
   (c) How many groups of eight are there?
   (d) How many crosses are left over?

2. (a) Copy the crosses.
   (b) Draw round groups of five.
   (c) How many groups of five are there?
   (d) How many crosses are left over?

3. Copy and complete:

   (a) 42_6 = ⬚ sixes + ⬚ units = ⬚ + ⬚ = ⬚ ten
   (b) 36_8 = ⬚ eights + ⬚ units = ⬚ + ⬚ = ⬚ ten

4. Balloons are put into packets of five.

   (a) How many balloons are there in 4 packets?
   (b) How many balloons are there if there are 3 packets and 4 balloons left over?
   (c) How many packets are needed to hold 15 balloons?
   (d) How many packets are needed and how many balloons are left over if there are 14 balloons?

5. Write the number 23_8 in base ten.

6. Write the number 54_8 in base ten.

A 1. How many days are there in 3 weeks?

2. How many days are there in four weeks and five days?

3. How many hours are there in 4 days?

4. Copy and complete:
   (a) $\frac{1}{2}$ h = $\boxed{?}$ min   (b) 1 h 25 min = $\boxed{?}$ min

5. Write 160 min in hours and minutes.

6. Copy and complete:
   (a) $1\frac{1}{2}$ min = $\boxed{?}$ s   (b) 2 min 10 s = $\boxed{?}$ s

7. Write 85 s in minutes and seconds.

8. A timer needs to be set for 1 h 45 min. How many minutes is that?

B 1. Write these 12-hour clock times using the 24-hour clock:
   (a) 9.00 a.m.   (b) 6.30 p.m.

2. Write these 24-hour clock times using the 12-hour clock:
   (a) 05.30   (b) 22.00

3. Copy these clocks. Make all three show the same time:
   (a)

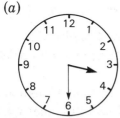

$\boxed{\qquad \text{a.m.}}$ in the 12-hour clock.

$\boxed{\qquad\qquad}$ in the 24-hour clock.

   (b)

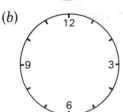

$\boxed{\qquad\qquad}$ in the 12-hour clock.

$\boxed{17.15}$ in the 24-hour clock.

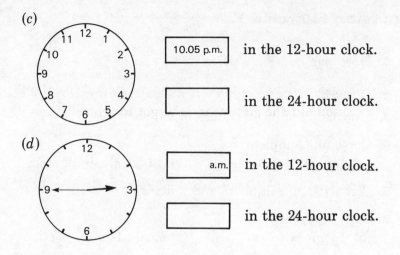

(c)

| 10.05 p.m. | in the 12-hour clock. |

| | in the 24-hour clock. |

(d)

| a.m. | in the 12-hour clock. |

| | in the 24-hour clock. |

4. Write in figures:
   (a) half past nine in the morning,
   (b) ten past seven in the evening.

5. Write in words:
   (a) 22.15   (b) 04.25

6. Write in figures:
   (a) quarter to eight in the morning,
   (b) twenty to two in the afternoon.

7. Write in words:
   (a) 03.55   (b) 20.50

8. How many minutes are there to the next hour if the time is now:
   (a) 12.35   (b) 14.15

9. Bill caught the bus at 14.50. His journey took 35 min. At what time did he get off the bus?

C 1. Use the timetable in Exercise 16 on p. 134.
- (*a*) On which day is the music lesson?
- (*b*) How long is the games lesson?
- (*c*) Lenka went to the dentist on Wednesday morning. She was then one hour and ten minutes late for school. Which lesson did she go to when she got to school?

2. Use the timetable on p. 136.
- (*a*) If you catch the 10.15 train from Manchester (Piccadilly), at what time do you arrive at London (Euston)?
- (*b*) If you want to arrive in Manchester (Piccadilly) at 14.35, at what time must you leave Stoke-on-Trent?

D 1. Which is the tenth month of the year?

2. How many days are there in May?

3. If the 14 March was a Wednesday on what day was the 23 March of the same year?

4. If it is Monday, 18 April what will next Monday's date be?

5. 4 January 1985 can be written 4.1.85.
- (*a*) Write in figures: 31 August 1984.
- (*b*) Write 19.2.79. using the name of the month.

6. Herma was thirteen years old on the 11 Dec 1984. When was she born?

7. Mr and Mrs Hall went on holiday on the 27 of July. They were away for 12 nights. What was the date of their return?

8. John went on holiday on the 28 May and returned on the 4 June. For how many nights was he on holiday?

1. Calculate the area of the rectangle:

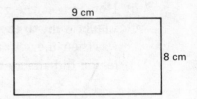

2. A rectangular garden is 18 m long and 9 m wide. Find its area.

3. Find the missing side of the rectangle:

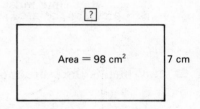

4. A rectangle has a perimeter of 42 m. If it is 13 m long, calculate its area.

5. (*a*) Copy the cuboid on dotty paper (triangular).

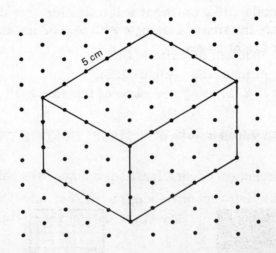

(*b*) Draw the net of the cuboid on squared paper.
(*c*) Calculate the surface area of the cuboid.

6. Calculate the area of the floor of a room that is 5 m long and 3.7 m wide.

7. Calculate the area of each parallelogram:

(a)   *(b)*

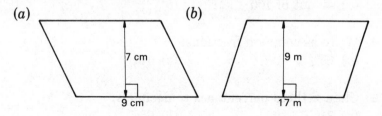

8. Calculate the area of each triangle:

(a)   *(b)*

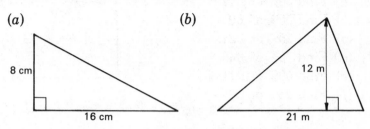

9. Calculate the area of a parallelogram with base 18 m and perpendicular height 13 m.

10. Calculate the area of a triangle with base 32 cm and perpendicular height 24 cm.

Revision Exercise XII

1. What percentage of each large square has been shaded?

(a)   *(b)*

2. (*a*) On squared paper, using 10 by 10 squares, shade:
   (*a*) 90%   (*b*) 35%

3. Write as percentages:
   (*a*) 42 out of 100   (*b*) $\frac{78}{100}$

4. Write as common fractions:
   (*a*) 69%   (*b*) 47%

5. Change these percentages to decimals:
   (*a*) 31%   (*b*) 68%

6. (*a*) Find 50% of £12.
   (*b*) Find 50% of £9.
   (*c*) Find 25% of £24.
   (*d*) Find 75% of £40.
   (*e*) Find 50% of £11.80.
   (*f*) Find 25% of £6.

13 Directed Numbers

Exercise 1

A **1.** What temperature is shown on the thermometer?

2. Is ⁻20 °C warmer than 10 °C?

3. Which is warmer, ⁻10 °C or 5 °C?

4. Which is colder, ⁻8 °C or ⁻6 °C?

5. Write these temperatures in order, from hottest to coldest:
8 °C, 0 °C, 27 °C, ⁻10 °C, 62 °C, ⁻8 °C, ⁻40 °C, 40 °C

B Here is a list of temperatures:

⁻4 °C   7 °C   28 °C   ⁻12 °C   42 °C   ⁻18 °C
13 °C   ⁻5 °C   ⁻25 °C   ⁻2 °C   36 °C   69 °C

1. Which is the third highest temperature in the list?

2. Which is the fourth lowest temperature in the list?

3. List the temperatures that are colder than ⁻10 °C. Choose from the list.

4. List the temperatures that are hotter than 35 °C. Choose from the list.

5. From the list, write the temperatures that lie between ⁻15 °C and 15 °C. List them in order, from coldest to hottest.

Exercise 2

Copy each of these number lines and fill in the missing numbers:

1.

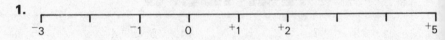

$^-3$ $^-1$ 0 $^+1$ $^+2$ $^+5$

2.

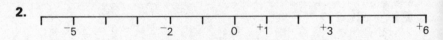

$^-5$ $^-2$ 0 $^+1$ $^+3$ $^+6$

3.

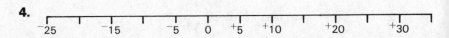

$^-60$ $^-40$ $^-10$ 0 $^+10$ $^+20$ $^+30$ $^+60$

4.

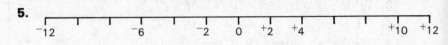

$^-25$ $^-15$ $^-5$ 0 $^+5$ $^+10$ $^+20$ $^+30$

5.

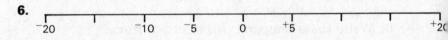

$^-12$ $^-6$ $^-2$ 0 $^+2$ $^+4$ $^+10$ $^+12$

6.

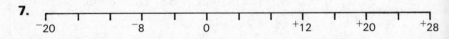

$^-20$ $^-10$ $^-5$ 0 $^+5$ $^+20$

7.

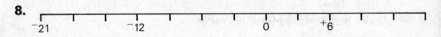

$^-20$ $^-8$ 0 $^+12$ $^+20$ $^+28$

8.

$^-21$ $^-12$ 0 $^+6$

9.

$^-30$ 0 $^+20$

10.

$^-26$ $^-22$ $^-18$ $^-12$ $^-8$ $^-4$ 0 $^+2$ $^+4$ $^+8$ $^+14$ $^+18$ $^+22$

11.

$^-11$ $^-9$ $^-6$ 0 $^+1$ $^+2$ $^+6$ $^+7$ $^+10$ $^+13$

12.

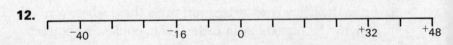

$^-40$ $^-16$ 0 $^+32$ $^+48$

Exercise 3

Copy each of the following and write whether it is true or false.
(You may use a number line.)

1. $^+3 < {}^+7$
2. $^-3 < {}^+7$
3. $^-3 < {}^-7$
4. $^+8 > {}^+5$
5. $^-5 > {}^-8$
6. $^-6 < {}^-4$
7. $^-2 > {}^-1$
8. $^+3 > {}^-3$
9. $^-4 > {}^-7$
10. $^-8 < {}^-5$

11. $^-5 < {}^+4$
12. $^-6 > {}^-5$
13. $^-7 < {}^-2$
14. $4 < 9$
15. $6 > {}^-3$
16. $^-5 > 2$
17. $^-5 < {}^-2$
18. $^-7 > {}^-1$
19. $^-6 < 0$
20. $^-5 < {}^-7$

Exercise 4

Copy these, but in place of each question mark use $<$ or $>$ to
make each statement correct:

1. $^-2 \boxed{?} {}^-5$
2. $^+6 \boxed{?} {}^-3$
3. $^+2 \boxed{?} {}^-6$
4. $^-5 \boxed{?} {}^+1$
5. $0 \boxed{?} {}^-4$
6. $^-7 \boxed{?} {}^-3$
7. $^-1 \boxed{?} {}^-6$
8. $^+3 \boxed{?} {}^-4$

9. $^+2 \boxed{?} {}^+8$
10. $^-9 \boxed{?} {}^-3$
11. $^-6 \boxed{?} 0$
12. $^-2 \boxed{?} {}^-8$
13. $^-1 \boxed{?} {}^-7$
14. $^-3 \boxed{?} {}^-1$
15. $^-6 \boxed{?} {}^-7$

177

Exercise 5

Write these numbers in order of size.
Put the smallest first.

1. $^+5$, $^+3$, $^+1$
2. $^-6$, $^+5$, $^-4$
3. $^-1$, $^-3$, $^-6$
4. $^-8$, $^-4$, $^-1$
5. 0, $^+2$, $^-6$

6. $^+7$, $^-7$, $^+5$, $^-3$
7. $^-6$, $^+4$, 0, $^-2$
8. $^-3$, $^-6$, $^+1$, $^+5$
9. $^-3$, $^-8$, $^-5$, $^-2$
10. 0, $^-9$, $^-1$, $^-6$, $^-3$

Exercise 6

1. Mr James had £40 in his bank account. If he wrote a cheque for £60, by much would he be overdrawn?

2 A submarine is at a depth of 1180 m. If it dives a further 260 m, what is its new depth?

3. An aeroplane is flying at 4800 m. If it loses height by 900 m, what is its new height?

4. An aeroplane was flying at 3500 m. If it falls to a height of 2800 m, what height was lost?

5. A submarine dives from a depth of 1470 m to a depth of 1820 m. By how many metres has it just dived?

6. Mrs Herrick is overdrawn at the bank by £30. If she spends a further £50, by how much would she then be overdrawn?

7. Mrs Wood had £60 in her bank account. She spent £50, deposited £25 then spent a further £70. By how much was she overdrawn?

8. If I have an overdraft of £30 at the bank, how much must I deposit to have a credit of £50?

Exercise 7

Use the number line to help you to answer these questions:

1. $5 + 4$	**26.** $5 - 3$
2. $^+6 + 8$	**27.** $^-5 - 3$
3. $3 + 12$	**28.** $^-7 - 6$
4. $^+2 + 7$	**29.** $2 + 6$
5. $^-2 + 7$	**30.** $^-2 + 6$
6. $^-4 + 9$	**31.** $^-6 + 2$
7. $0 + 13$	**32.** $6 - 2$
8. $^-5 + 17$	**33.** $2 - 6$
9. $8 - 3$	**34.** $^-2 - 6$
10. $11 - 9$	**35.** $^-6 - 2$
11. $13 - 4$	**36.** $4 + 7 - 3$
12. $^+12 - 8$	**37.** $9 - 4 + 2$
13. $^+9 - 5$	**38.** $12 - 4 - 3$
14. $17 - 11$	**39.** $^-2 + 4 + 1$
15. $13 - 7$	**40.** $5 + 2 - 9$
16. $4 - 2$	**41.** $3 - 4 - 5$
17. $2 - 4$	**42.** $^-4 + 2 + 7$
18. $6 - 9$	**43.** $^-7 + 1 + 3$
19. $7 - 7$	**44.** $^-9 + 4 - 1$
20. $9 - 9$	**45.** $^-8 + 10 - 2$
21. $8 - 15$	**46.** $14 - 3 + 3$
22. $^+6 - 13$	**47.** $17 + 6 - 6 - 8$
23. $^+7 - 11$	**48.** $^-9 + 9 + 5$
24. $1 - 16$	**49.** $^-11 + 8 - 5 + 11$
25. $3 - 19$	**50.** $^-14 - 5 + 2 + 14$

$^+16$
$^+15$
$^+14$
$^+13$
$^+12$
$^+11$
$^+10$
$^+9$
$^+8$
$^+7$
$^+6$
$^+5$
$^+4$
$^+3$
$^+2$
$^+1$
0
$^-1$
$^-2$
$^-3$
$^-4$
$^-5$
$^-6$
$^-7$
$^-8$
$^-9$
$^-10$
$^-11$
$^-12$
$^-13$
$^-14$
$^-15$
$^-16$
$^-17$
$^-18$
$^-19$
$^-20$

Exercise 8

Use a calculator to check your answers to Exercise 7.

An example is given on page 180.

e.g. $^-7 - 6 = \boxed{?}$

If your calculator has a $\boxed{^+/_-}$ key then $^-7 - 6$ should probably be worked out as follows:

$\boxed{AC}\boxed{7}\boxed{^+/_-}\boxed{-}\boxed{6}\boxed{=}$ which gives $^-13$

If your calculator does not have a $\boxed{^+/_-}$ key then you need to work out $0 - 7 - 6$ as follows:

$\boxed{AC}\boxed{0}\boxed{-}\boxed{7}\boxed{-}\boxed{6}\boxed{=}$ which also gives $^-13$

Exercise 9 M

Copy and complete this table:

	Original temperature	Rise in temperature	New temperature
1.	7 °C	2 °C	
2.	5 °C	7 °C	
3.	$^-4$ °C	7 °C	
4.	$^-8$ °C	12 °C	
5.	6 °C		10 °C
6.		4 °C	9 °C
7.	$^-5$ °C		2 °C
8.		8 °C	12 °C
9.		8 °C	2 °C
10.	$^-8$ °C	8 °C	
11.	$^-2$ °C		0 °C
12.	14 °C	17 °C	
13.	$^-8$ °C	5 °C	
14.	$^-5$ °C		5 °C
15.		7 °C	$^-9$ °C

180

Exercise 10

Copy and complete this table:

	Original temperature	Fall in temperature	New temperature
1.	13 °C	6 °C	
2.	8 °C	3 °C	
3.	9 °C	12 °C	
4.	4 °C	10 °C	
5.	12 °C		9 °C
6.		5 °C	6 °C
7.	⁻3 °C	4 °C	
8.	⁻9 °C	2 °C	
9.	⁻4 °C		⁻7 °C
10.		7 °C	⁻3 °C
11.	7 °C	7 °C	
12.		6 °C	0 °C
13.	8 °C		⁻8 °C
14.		8 °C	⁻12 °C
15.	⁻13 °C		⁻21 °C

Exercise 11

4↑ means 'a journey 4 places up'.

3↓ means 'a journey 3 places down'.

6↑ + 2↓ can be read as 'a journey 6 places up *followed by* a journey 2 places down'.

e.g. 1 6↑ + 2↓ = <u><u>4↑</u></u>

e.g. 2 4↓ + 2↑ = <u><u>2↓</u></u>

Answer these questions. Use the number line.

1.	3↑ + 2↑	**19.**	8↑ + 2↑
2.	6↑ + 3↓	**20.**	8↓ + 2↓
3.	7↑ + 5↓	**21.**	4↑ + 4↓
4.	9↑ + 2↑	**22.**	4↑ + 4↑
5.	2↑ + 7↓	**23.**	4↓ + 4↓
6.	6↑ + 8↓	**24.**	11↑ + 5↓
7.	2↓ + 9↑	**25.**	7↑ + 3↓
8.	10↓ + 4↑	**26.**	17↑ + 13↓
9.	3↓ + 3↑	**27.**	9↑ + 4↓
10.	6↑ + 6↓	**28.**	10↑ + 5↓
11.	8↑ + 5↓	**29.**	8↑ + 3↓
12.	8↓ + 5↑	**30.**	6↑ + 7↑ + 3↓
13.	8↑ + 5↑	**31.**	3↑ + 6↓ + 4↑
14.	8↓ + 5↓	**32.**	4↓ + 7↑ + 1↑
15.	8↑ + 2↓	**33.**	8↓ + 5↓ + 4↑
16.	2↓ + 8↑	**34.**	12↑ + 7↓ + 5↓
17.	2↑ + 8↓	**35.**	9↑ + 8↓ + 6↑
18.	8↓ + 2↑	**36.**	7↓ + 7↑ + 5↑

+16
+15
+14
+13
+12
+11
+10
+9
+8
+7
+6
+5
+4
+3
+2
+1
0
−1
−2
−3
−4
−5
−6
−7
−8
−9
−10
−11
−12
−13
−14
−15
−16
−17
−18
−19
−20

14 Relations Between Two Sets

Felicia *is taller than* John.

The sentence above shows a *relation* between two people. The relation is: 'is taller than'.

John   Felicia

Age	12 years	13 years
Height	1.49 m	1.57 m
Mass	45.1 kg	43.6 kg

Write three sentences of your own about Felicia and John. In each sentence, underline the relation.

Exercise 2

The relation 'is the son of' for a set of sons and a set of mothers is shown.

We can write

'Angus *is the son of* Mrs Stewart'

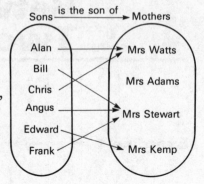

1. Write three sentences of your own showing the relation between the two given sets.

2. How many sons has Mrs Stewart if all her sons are given here?

3. Which mother has no sons?

Exercise 3

The relation 'likes' for a set of people and a set of drinks is given.

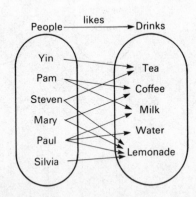

1. How many liked coffee?

2. Which drink did most people like?

3. Who liked the most drinks?

4. Which drinks did Mary like?

5. Which drink did only one person like?

Copy and complete the relation diagrams:

1.

is half of

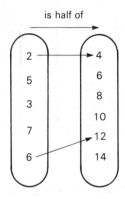

4.

is
bigger than
Animals ──────► Animals

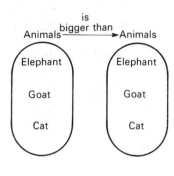

2.

is the capital of
City ──────► Country

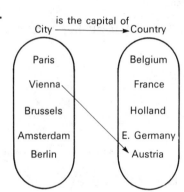

5.

in the alphabet,
comes before

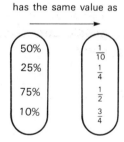

6.

has the same value as

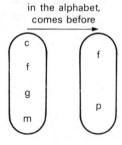

3.

is 3 more than

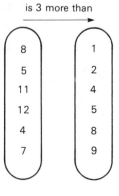

7.

has the same
number of digits as

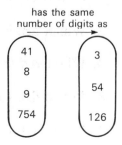

185

8.

is double
→

18	2
4	4
8	5
10	6
24	9
	12

11.

is a factor of
→

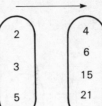

2	4
3	6
5	15
	21

9.

surname begins
with the same letters as
→

Miller	Walker
Wong	Moore
Andrews	Wells
Mitchell	Davies
Davis	Addison

12.

is less than
→

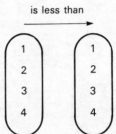

1	1
2	2
3	3
4	4

10.

gives 10 when added to
→

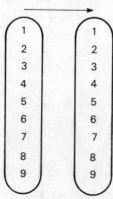

1	1
2	2
3	3
4	4
5	5
6	6
7	7
8	8
9	9

Exercise 5

For each question two sets are given and a rule. Show each relation on a diagram as in Exercise 4:

1. $A = \{3, 5, 6, 9, 12, 14\}$, $B = \{5, 11, 8, 14, 7, 16\}$

Relation: 'is 2 less than' from set A to set B.

2. $F = \{$Mr Taylor, Mr Jones, Mr Stuart, Mr Ryan$\}$

$S = \{$Andrew Stuart, Shaun Ryan, Owen Jones, James Stuart, Pamela Taylor, Lorna Jones$\}$

Relation: 'is the father of' from set F to set S.

3. $P = \{4 \times 3, 10 \times 2, 2 \times 8, 6 \times 5, 6 \times 6\}$

$Q = \{5 \times 4, 3 \times 10, 2 \times 6, 4 \times 9, 4 \times 4\}$

Relation: 'has the same product as' from set P to set Q.

Exercise 6   M

1. (a) Copy and complete the *mapping diagram*.

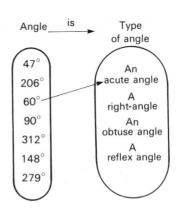

(b) 60° *maps to* an acute angle.
What maps to an obtuse angle?

(c) What does 90° map to?

(d) Which angles map to a reflex angle?

187

2. (a) Copy and complete the mapping diagram.

(b) Which polygon maps to 6?

(c) What does the pentagon map to?

(d) Which polygons map to the same number?

Polygon ——has——► Number of sides

Pentagon	3
Triangle	4
Square	5
Octagon	6
Rhombus	7
Hexagon	8

Exercise 7

1. If $n = 3$, find the value of:
(a) $n + 6$ (d) $n + 9$ (g) $5n$
(b) $n + 4$ (e) $2n$ (h) $2n + 1$
(c) $n - 1$ (f) $4n$ (i) $2n + 5$

2. Find the value of:
(a) $k + 3$ when $k = 6$ (e) $3u$ when $u = 10$
(b) $x + 8$ when $x = 4$ (f) $l + 10$ when $l = 7$
(c) $m - 5$ when $m = 9$ (g) $2p + 6$ when $p = 5$
(d) $2t$ when $t = 7$ (h) $2g - 5$ when $g = 6$

Exercise 8   M

Copy and complete the following mapping diagrams:

1. $x \xrightarrow{\text{add 4}} (x + 4)$

0	► ?
1	► ?
2	► ?
3	► 7
4	► ?

2.

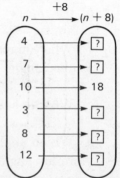

$n \xrightarrow{+8} (n + 8)$

4	► ?
7	► ?
10	► 18
3	► ?
8	► ?
12	► ?

3.

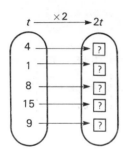

4.

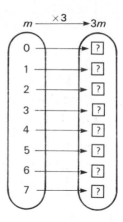

Exercise 9

Copy and complete these mapping diagrams. Answer the questions given.

1.

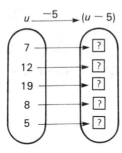

(a) What does 12 map to?

(b) What maps to 2?

(c) What maps to 0?

2.

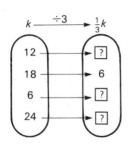

(a) What does 24 map to?

(b) What maps to 2?

(c) What maps to 4?

3. The rule for the mapping is 'double then add 1'.

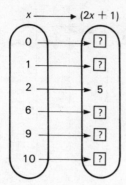

(a) What does 0 map to?

(b) What maps to 3?

(c) What maps to 17?

4.

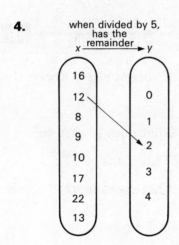

(a) What does 9 map to?

(b) What maps to 0?

(c) What maps to 2?

15 Co-ordinates and Graphs

Exercise 1

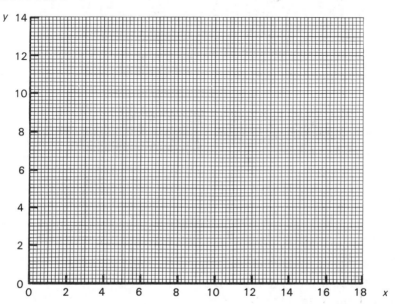

Draw a pair of axes as shown.
Label the x-axis from 0 to 18.
Label the y-axis from 0 to 14.

Plot and join each pair of points.
Write the co-ordinates of the mid-point of the straight line that joins each pair of points:

1. (2, 10) (2, 14)   **6.** (4, 14) (16, 10)
2. (12, 13) (18, 13)   **7.** (2, 2) (8, 4)
3. (6, 9) (10, 11)   **8.** (5, 9) (11, 3)
4. (12, 2) (16, 8)   **9.** (16, 6) (18, 0)
5. (8, 8) (12, 6)   **10.** (4, 8) (0, 0)

Exercise 2

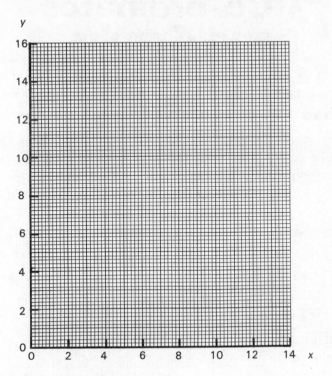

Draw a pair of axes as shown.
Label the *x*-axis from 0 to 14.
Label the *y*-axis from 0 to 16.

Answer all the following questions using the same pair of axes:

1. Plot the three points (8, 2), (12, 2) and (12, 4) and join them with straight lines in that order. Find the fourth point to give a rectangle.

2. Use straight lines to join (4, 13) to (4, 15) to (2, 15). Find the fourth point to give a square.

3. Use straight lines to join (14, 16) to (10, 16) to (8, 14). Find the fourth point to give a parallelogram.

4. Plot the three points (4, 0) (2, 2) and (4, 4) and join them with straight lines in that order. Find the fourth point to give a square.

5. Join $(12, 7)$ to $(7, 6)$ to $(8, 8)$ using straight lines. Find the fourth point to give a parallelogram.

6. Join $(2, 11)$ to $(3, 9)$ to $(7, 11)$ using straight lines. Find the fourth point to give a rectangle.

7. Join $(8, 11)$ to $(8, 13)$ to $(14, 13)$ to $(14, 11)$ to $(8, 11)$ to form a rectangle. Draw both diagonals of this rectangle. Write the point of intersection of the diagonals.

8. Join $(1, 6)$ to $(2, 9)$ to $(5, 8)$ to $(4, 5)$ to $(1, 6)$ to form a square. Draw both diagonals of this square. Write the point of intersection of the diagonals.

Exercise 3

Draw a pair of axes as shown. Use a scale of 1 cm to 1 unit on both axes.

Label the x-axis from $^-8$ to $^+8$.

Label the y-axis from $^-10$ to $^+10$.

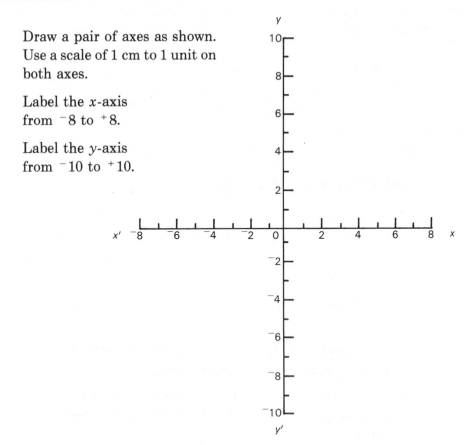

Answer all the following on the same piece of graph paper using the same pair of axes.

For each question, plot the points and join them in the order given. Inside each shape, print its name.

Choose the correct name from the set:

{square, rectangle, rhombus, kite, parallelogram, trapezium, isosceles triangle, equilateral triangle, pentagon, hexagon, octagon}

1. (1, 2) (1, 4) (4, 4) (4, 2) (1, 2)
2. (⁻4, 8) (⁻4, 6) (⁻2, 6) (⁻2, 8) (⁻4, 8)
3. (8, ⁻5) (7, ⁻7) (3, ⁻7) (4, ⁻5) (8, ⁻5)
4. (0, 7) (6, 9) (6, 5) (0, 7)
5. (⁻6, ⁻4) (⁻7, ⁻5) (⁻6, ⁻8) (⁻5, ⁻5) (⁻6, ⁻4)
6. (7, ⁻1) (5, 1) (3, ⁻1) (5, ⁻3) (7, ⁻1)
7. (⁻7, 0) (⁻7, 3) (⁻4, 5) (⁻1, 3) (⁻1, 0) (⁻4, ⁻2) (⁻7, 0)
8. (2, ⁻9) (⁻5, ⁻9) (⁻3, ⁻6) (1, ⁻6) (2, ⁻9)

Exercise 4

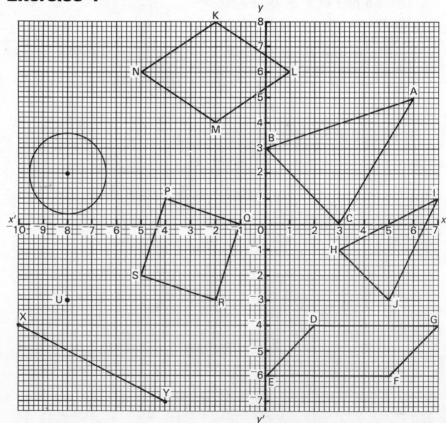

1. In $\triangle$ABC, which vertex is at $(0, 3)$?

2. In square PQRS, do the diagonals intersect at $(3, {}^-1)$ or at $({}^-3, {}^-1)$?

3. Write the co-ordinates of the vertices of the rhombus.

4. (a) What are the co-ordinates of the centre of the circle?
   (b) Which point lies inside the circle? $({}^-7, 2)$ $({}^-7, {}^-2)$ $(7, 2)$ or $(7, {}^-2)$

5. On which side of the parallelogram does the point $(4, {}^-6)$ lie?

6. Which point lies on side IJ of the isosceles triangle? $(5, 0)$ $(4, {}^-2)$ $({}^-2, 4)$ $({}^-1, 6)$ or $(6, {}^-1)$

7. XY is parallel to UV. Line XY and point U are shown. Is V at $({}^-4, {}^-5)$ or at $({}^-3, {}^-5)$?

Exercise 5   M

1. Copy and complete the mapping diagram below for the relation 'is 3 less than:'

   is
   $x \xrightarrow{\text{3 less than}} y$

x	y
0	→ 3
1	→ 4
2	→ ?
3	→ ?
4	→ ?
5	→ 8
6	→ ?
7	→10

2. Copy and complete the pairs of co-ordinates below. Use the mapping diagram to help you.

   $(0, \ 3 \ )$
   $(1, \ 4 \ )$
   $(2, \boxed{?} \ )$
   $(3, \boxed{?} \ )$
   $(4, \boxed{?} \ )$
   $(5, \ 8 \ )$
   $(6, \boxed{?} \ )$
   $(7, \ 10 \ )$

3. Make out a table from the pairs of co-ordinates:

x	y
0	3
1	4
2	
3	
4	
5	8
6	
7	10

4. (*a*) Now draw a pair of axes as shown.
Use a scale of 2 cm to 1 unit

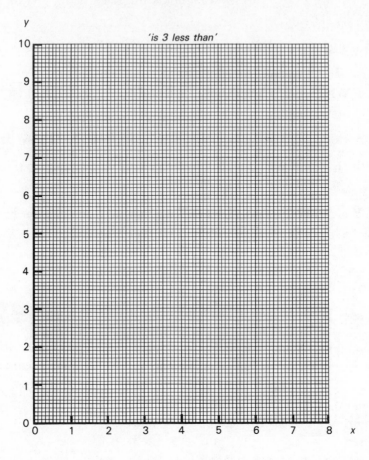

(*b*) Plot the points that you have written in question 2.
Note that the same points could have been plotted from the table in question 3.

(*c*) Join the points you have plotted.

(*d*) Write what you notice about the graph you have just drawn.

For each question, copy and complete the mapping diagram, the pairs of co-ordinates and the table for the relation given:

1. 'is 4 less than'

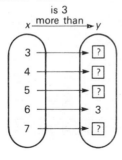

(0, ?)
(1, ?)
(4, ?)
(5, 9)
(7, ?)
(8, ?)

x	y
0	
1	
4	
5	9
7	
8	

2. 'is 3 more than'

(3, ?)
(4, ?)
(5, ?)
(6, 3)
(7, ?)

x	y
3	
4	
5	
6	3
7	

3. 'is one-third of'

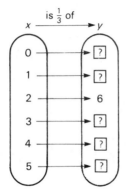

(0, ?)
(1, ?)
(2, 6)
(3, ?)
(4, ?)
(5, ?)

x	y
0	
1	
2	6
3	
4	
5	

1. 'is 2 less than'

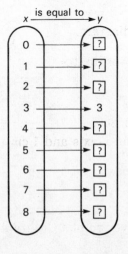

x	y
0	
1	
2	
3	5
4	
5	
6	
7	
8	

(0, ?)
(1, ?)
(2, ?)
(3, 5)
(4, ?)
(5, ?)
(6, ?)
(7, ?)
(8, ?)

(a) Copy and complete the mapping diagram.
(b) Copy and complete the pairs of co-ordinates.
(c) Copy and complete the table.
(d) Draw a pair of axes as in Exercise 5, question 4 on p. 196.
(e) Draw a graph of the relation 'is 2 less than'.

2. 'is equal to'

x	y
0	
1	
2	
3	3
4	
5	
6	
7	
8	

(0, ?)
(1, ?)
(2, ?)
(3, 3)
(4, ?)
(5, ?)
(6, ?)
(7, ?)
(8, ?)

(a) Copy and complete the bottom mapping diagram on p. 198.

(b) Copy and complete the pairs of co-ordinates.

(c) Copy and complete the table.

(d) Draw another pair of axes as in question 1.

(e) Draw a graph of the relation 'is equal to'.

3. 'is half'

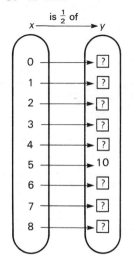

(0, ?)

(1, ?)

(2, ?)

(3, ?)

(4, ?)

(5, 10)

(6, ?)

(7, ?)

(8, ?)

x	y
0	
1	
2	
3	
4	
5	10
6	
7	
8	

(a) Copy and complete the mapping diagram.

(b) Copy and complete the pairs of co-ordinates.

(c) Copy and complete the table.

(d) Draw a pair of axes as shown on p. 200.
    Use a scale of 2 cm to 1 unit on the x-axis and 1 cm to 1 unit on the y-axis.

(e) Graph the relation 'is half of'.

Note how the table can be used to help you to plot the graph.

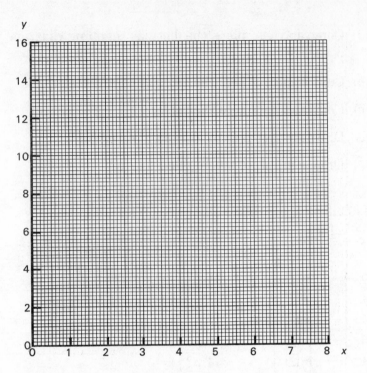

Exercise 8 M

1. Pens cost £2 each. The table below shows the cost of buying up to 8 pens.

   (a) Copy and complete the table.

Number of pens, n	Cost of pens (£)
0	0
1	2
2	4
3	
4	
5	10
6	
7	
8	16

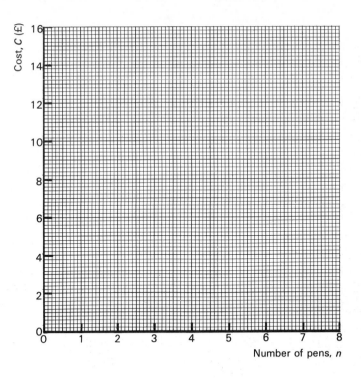

(b) Draw a pair of axes as shown. Use a scale of 2 cm to 1 pen on the *horizontal axis* and 1 cm to £1 on the *vertical axis*.

(c) Use the table opposite to help you to draw a graph.

(d) Compare your graph with the graph in question 3(e) of Exercise 7 on p. 199.

2. I travelled at 50 m.p.h. The table shows how far I travelled each hour up to a total of 8 h.

Time taken, t (h)	0	1	2	3	4	5	6	7	8
Distance travelled, s (miles)	0	50	100			250			400

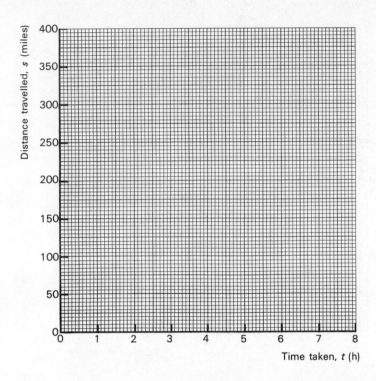

(a) Copy and complete the table on the previous page.

(b) Draw a pair of axes as shown. Use a scale of 2 cm to 1 h on the *horizontal axis* and 1 cm to 25 miles on the *vertical axis*.

(c) Use the table to help you to draw the graph.

16 Circumference of a Circle

Exercise 1

A Write the diameter and the radius of each of these circles. (They are not drawn to size.)

1.

14 cm

4.

30 mm

7.

32 cm

2.

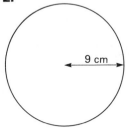

9 cm

5.

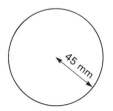

45 mm

8.

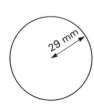

29 mm

3.

20 mm

6.

86 mm

9.

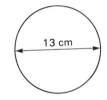

13 cm

10.

$2\frac{1}{2}$ m

11.

1.9 m

12.

7.4 cm

B Copy and complete:

1. The diameter is t – – – – the radius.

2. The radius is h – – – the diameter.

Exercise 2

For this exercise you need several cylindrical objects such as jars, tins, coins and so on. They should be different sizes.

Find the diameter and the circumference of each circular base (or cross-section) of each object you have collected.

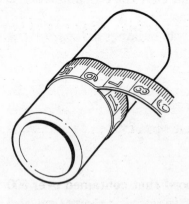

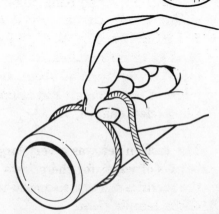

To find the circumference either wrap a tape measure around the object or wrap a piece of string around it, then measure the length of the string (or use a method of your own).

Show your results in a table as follows:

Object	Circumference, C	Diameter, d	$\dfrac{C}{d}$

Complete the last column by dividing the circumference by the diameter. (Use a calculator.)
Write what you notice.

From Exercise 2 you probably found that the circumference is slightly more than 3 times the diameter.
In the Bible, when King Solomon was building his temple, the circumference was thought to be three times the diameter.
In I Kings, chap. 7, vs. 23, it says:
'And he made a molten sea ten cubits from the one brim to the other: it was round all about, and its height was five cubits: and a line of thirty cubits did compass it round about.' (See also II Chronicles, chap. 4, vs. 2.)

The molten sea was a very large bowl that contained over 500 barrels of water for the priests' use in washing themselves and the sacrifices. They also used the water for keeping the courts of the temple clean.

Exercise 3

Find the circumference of each circle:

Use: Circumference, $C \approx 3d$

e.g.   Diameter, $d = 6$ cm

Circumference, $C \approx 3d$

$$= 3 \times 6$$

∴   the circumference = <u>18 cm</u>

6 cm

1.
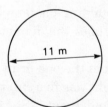
9 cm

5.

50 mm

2.

5 cm

6.

43 mm

3.
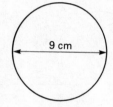
11 m

7.

8.9 cm

4.

30 mm

8.

9.7 cm

Exercise 4

Find the circumference of each circle.

Use: Circumference $\approx 3d$

e.g.

Radius, r = 2.4 m

Diameter, d = 4.8 m

Circumference, $C \approx 3d$

$$= 3 \times 4.8$$

$\therefore$ the circumference = 14.4 m

2.4 m

1.

5 cm

5.

3.5 m

2.

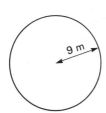

2 m

6.

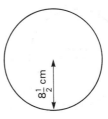

20 mm

3.

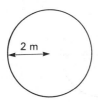

9 m

7.

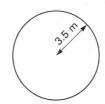

$8\frac{1}{2}$ cm

4.

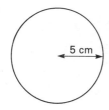

1.5 cm

8.

2.7 cm

Exercise 5

Find the circumference of each circle.

Use: Circumference ≈ 3d

1.

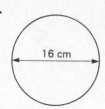

16 cm

6.

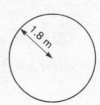

1.8 m

2.

1 m

7.

4.6 cm

3.

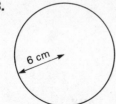

6 cm

8.

7.8 m

4.

60 mm

9.

34 mm

5.

45 mm

10.

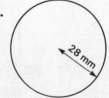

28 mm

Exercise 6

Use: Circumference $\approx 3d$ in this exercise:

1. Find the circumference of this pedal bin:

Diameter = 24 cm

2. Find the length of the wired rim of the paint tin:

Wired rim

Diameter = 15 cm

3. How long is the label that fits exactly around a tin of soup if the tin has a diameter of 75 mm?

4. What length of frill is needed to go once around a Christmas cake with a diameter of 8 in?

5. A label goes half-way around a jam jar. If the jam jar has a diameter of 66 mm, how long is the label?

6. A circular cycle track has a radius of 70 m. How far does a cyclist travel in 8 laps?

7. A bicycle wheel has a diameter of 27 in.
- (a) How far will a cyclist travel if the wheels turn 100 times? (Give the answer in inches.)
- (b) Change the answer into yards. Since 1 yd = 36 in, divide the answer in part (a) by 36. (Use a calculator.)

8. The label of a coffee jar goes once around the jar and overlaps itself by 10 mm. How long is the label if the diameter of the jar is 85 mm?

17 **Transformation Geometry**

We live in a world where many things move. It can be useful to study how they move.

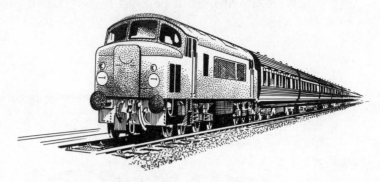

A train travelling on straight railway tracks

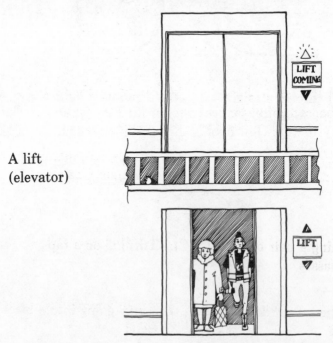

A lift
(elevator)

People on an
escalator

The movements shown above are alike in some way.
They show movement in a straight line.
We call movement in a straight line a *translation*.
The movement may be in any direction but must be in a straight
line.
The object being moved must not turn.
The shape and size of the object do not change but its position
does.

Exercise 1

Which of these are translations?

A. The movement of a
snooker cue

B. A ball thrown straight
upwards into the air

C. The movement of a bolt on
a door

D. Opening a pair of
compasses

E. Taking a record out of its
sleeve

F. The movement of a rope in
a tug-of-war

G. Climbing a ladder

H. A skater skating in
a straight line

I. Turning on a tap

J. A nail going into a piece of
wood

A wheelbarrow being tipped shows a different type of movement. It turns about a point. This type of movement is called a *rotation*.

A tap needs to be turned (another example of a rotation). Once again, the shape and size of the object do not change but its position does.

Exercise 2

Which of these are rotations?

A. Unscrewing the top of a jar

B. Turning a door knob or handle

C. Sharpening a pencil in a pencil sharpener

D. Moving the steering wheel of a car

E. Sliding a tray into an oven

F. Opening a desk lid

G. The movement of a hand of a clock

H. Pulling a book from a full bookshelf

I. The movement of a light switch when a light is switched on

J. A conker being swung in a game of conkers

If you look in a mirror you see a *reflection* of yourself. You have not moved but your image is in a different position. Your shape and size have not changed. The image can be seen of any object placed in front of a mirror. Any point on the object maps to a similar point on the image.

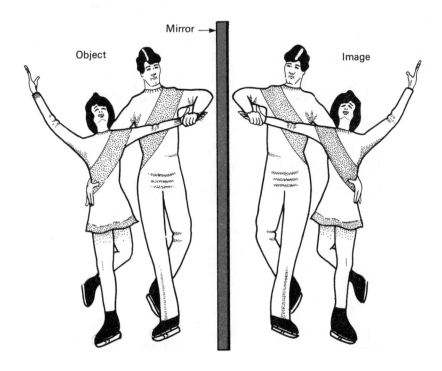

Object   Mirror ⟶   Image

An object can be drawn and its image can be drawn in a different position.

For translations and rotations we can also use the words object and image. Look at the train on p. 212. The original position is called the object and the new position is called the image.

Each point on the object maps to a similar point on the image (as for reflections).

Look at the wheelbarrow opposite. The original position is called the object and the new position is called the image. For rotations, each point on the object maps to a similar point on the image.

With translations, reflections and rotations changes have happened, i.e. each point on the object has been mapped to a new position (the image position).

Translations, reflections and rotations are called *transformations*. A transformation is the relation between each point on an object and its image point.

Exercise 3

e.g. The movement of a snooker cue during a game is a translation.

A For each of these movements, write the type of transformation: translation, reflection or rotation:

1. An aeroplane as it taxies along a runway

2. The movement of a tennis racket when the player is serving

3. The closing of a door that is on hinges

4. The opening of a sliding window

5. The opening of a book

6. The turning of a key in a lock

7. Opening a drawer

8. The movement of the drum in a washing machine

B 1. Write two examples of a translation.

2. Write two examples of a rotation.

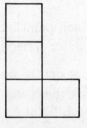

Make a copy of this L-shape.
Cut out your copy. (It may be better made out of card.)
Use your L-shape in the following exercises.

Translations

Exercise 4

The L-shape has been translated to four different positions:

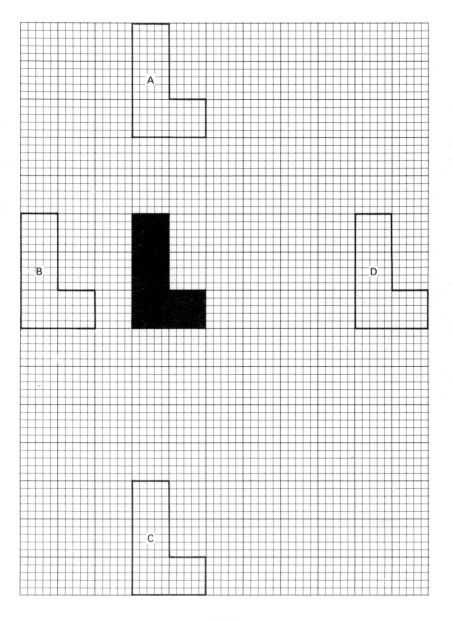

The image positions are A, B, C and D. Choose A, B, C or D to complete these:

1. A translation 6 cm to the right is ? .

2. A translation 3 cm to the left is ? .

3. A translation 5 cm up is ? .

4. A translation 7 cm down is ? .

Exercise 5

Place your L-shape on to a piece of graph paper or on to 1 cm squared paper. Draw round it.

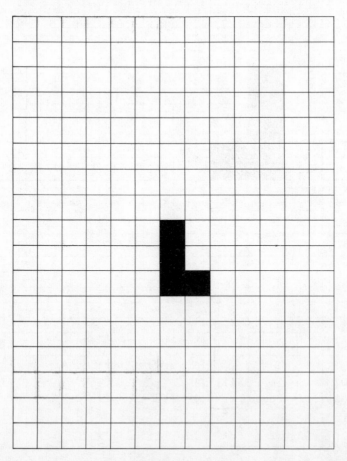

1. Translate it 4 cm to the right. Draw round it. Label this new position P. (This new position is an image of the first position.)

2. Place your L-shape at the first position again. Translate it 6 cm down. Draw round it. Label this position Q.

3. Place your L-shape at the first position again. Translate it 8 cm up. Draw round it. Label this position R.

4. Place your L-shape at the first position again. Translate it 5 cm to the left. Draw round it. Label this position S.

Reflections | ꙅⁿoᴉⱶɔǝlⱡǝЯ

1. Place your L-shape on top of the shaded L below. Reflect your L in the mirror line (a mirror or a piece of coloured perspex may help).

2. Copy the given L and the mirror line on to squared paper (or graph paper). Draw the image on your paper.

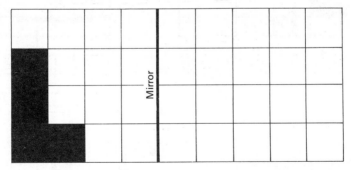

3. Draw another L, as shown on p. 220, on a different part of your piece of squared paper (or graph paper).
   Draw the mirror, m.
   Reflect the L in the mirror.
   Draw its image.

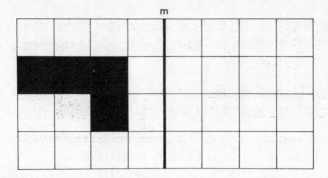

Exercise 7 ======================================= **M**

On graph paper or on 1 cm squared paper, draw the given L-shapes and 2-sided mirrors. For each one, reflect the L-shape in the given mirror and draw its image. Use the L-shape you made to help you.

Note that the given drawings are not full size.

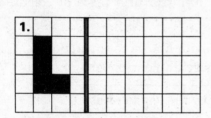

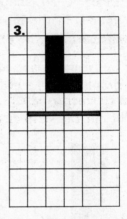

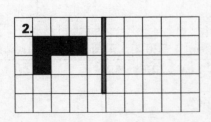

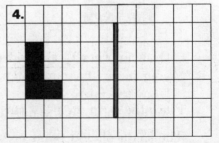

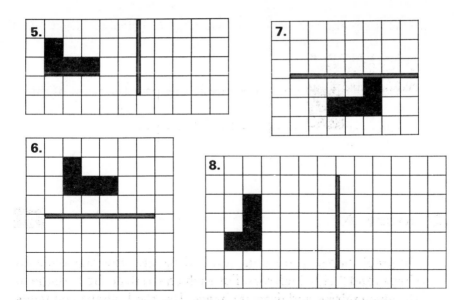

Rotations

Exercise 8

Copy the shape and straight line on to a piece of graph paper or on to tracing paper.

Cut out the strip of paper with the shape on it.

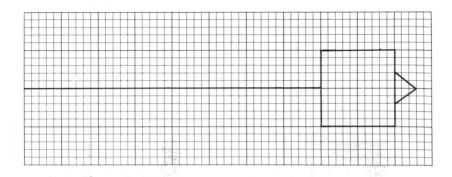

Place the strip on a flat surface.

The shape should point across as shown.

1. Put the point of a pencil anywhere on the straight line that is on your piece of paper.

   Rotate the shape $\frac{1}{4}$ of a turn clockwise about the point of the pencil.
   Which way is the shape now facing:
   A, B, C or D?

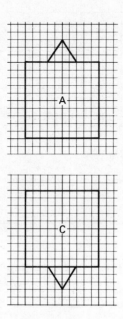 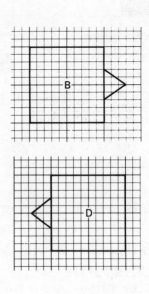

2. Put the point of the pencil somewhere else on the straight line. Point the shape across.
   Again rotate the shape $\frac{1}{4}$ of a turn clockwise.
   Which way is the shape now facing:
   A, B, C or D?

3. Try other positions on the straight line.
   Point the shape as before then rotate it $\frac{1}{4}$ of a turn clockwise.
   Write what you notice about all your answers.

In this exercise, use the strip of paper with the shape on it (from Exercise 8 on p. 221.)

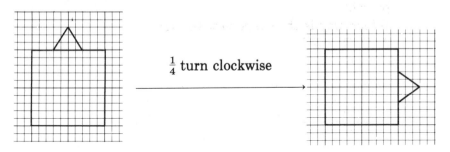

$\frac{1}{4}$ turn clockwise

The mapping above is true. For each of these mappings, write whether it is true or false:

1.

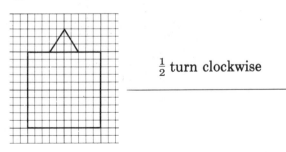

$\frac{1}{2}$ turn clockwise

2.

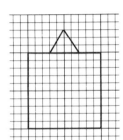

$\frac{1}{4}$ turn anticlockwise

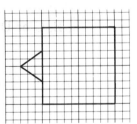

3.

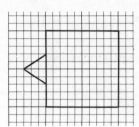 $\frac{1}{4}$ turn anticlockwise $\longrightarrow$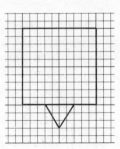

4.

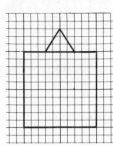 $\frac{1}{2}$ turn anticlockwise $\longrightarrow$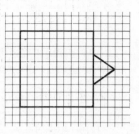

5.

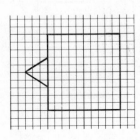 $\frac{3}{4}$ turn clockwise $\longrightarrow$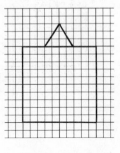

6.

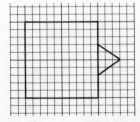 $\frac{3}{4}$ turn anticlockwise $\longrightarrow$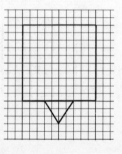

Exercise 10

For each transformation, draw the final position of the shape:

1. A $\frac{1}{2}$ turn anticlockwise

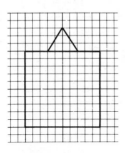

4. A $\frac{1}{4}$ turn anticlockwise

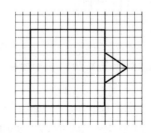

2. A $\frac{3}{4}$ turn clockwise

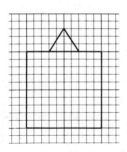

5. A $\frac{1}{4}$ turn clockwise

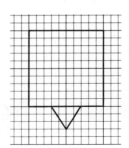

3. A full turn clockwise

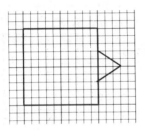

6. A $\frac{3}{4}$ turn clockwise

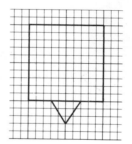

7. A $\frac{1}{4}$ turn clockwise

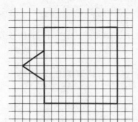

8. A $\frac{3}{4}$ turn anticlockwise

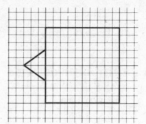

Exercise 11

A bottle top is rotated when the bottle is opened or closed. The centre of rotation lies on the top itself.

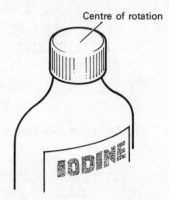

Centre of rotation

1.

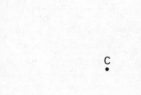

C

(*a*) Trace the square and mark the point C.

(*b*) Copy the square into your exercise book.

(*c*) Place your tracing on top of your drawn copy of the square.

Put a pencil point on the tracing paper at C.

Rotate the tracing clockwise until the traced square fits exactly on top of the drawn square again.

Check that it made one full turn.

2. (*a*) Make another tracing of the square. DO NOT mark point C.

(*b*) Draw the two diagonals on your traced square.

(*c*) Place your tracing on top of your drawn copy of the square.

Put a pencil point on the tracing paper at the centre of the square.

Rotate the tracing clockwise until the traced square fits exactly on top of the drawn square again.

Through what fraction of a turn has the traced square turned?

Through how many degrees has it turned?

18 Indices and Number Patterns

Exercise 1

Write in index form:

e.g. 1 $7 \times 7 \times 7 = \underline{\underline{7^3}}$

e.g. 2 $x \times x \times x \times x \times x = \underline{\underline{x^5}}$

1. $m \times m \times m \times m$

2. $y \times y \times y \times y \times y \times y$

3. $8 \times 8 \times 8 \times 8 \times 8$

4. $9 \times 9 \times 9$

5. $a \times a$

6. $4 \times 4 \times 4 \times 4 \times 4 \times 4 \times 4 \times 4 \times 4$

7. $3 \times 3 \times 3 \times 3 \times 3 \times 3 \times 3$

8. $t \times t \times t \times t \times t \times t \times t \times t$

9. $d \times d \times d$

10. $n \times n \times n \times n \times n \times n \times n \times n \times n$

Exercise 2

Find the value of:

1. 1^2	**5.** 5^2	**9.** 9^2
2. 2^2	**6.** 6^2	**10.** 10^2
3. 3^2	**7.** 7^2	**11.** 11^2
4. 4^2	**8.** 8^2	**12.** 12^2

Exercise 3

Find the value of:

e.g. $2^6 = 2 \times 2 \times 2 \times 2 \times 2 \times 2$

so $\quad 2^6 = \underline{\underline{64}}$

1. 2^3 **4.** 5^4 **7.** 10^4

2. 2^5 **5.** 3^4 **8.** 8^3

3. 5^3 **6.** 6^3

Exercise 4

1. Find the value of x^3 when $x = 4$.

2. If $c = 2$, find the value of c^7.

3. If $V = l^3$, find V when $l = 3$.

4. If $A = l^2$, find A when $l = 15$.

5. If $A = 6a^2$, find A when $a = 5$.

Exercise 5

Fold a piece of paper in half. (A sheet of newspaper will do.) After one fold it is 2 sheets thick.
Fold it in half again.

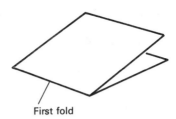

First fold

After two folds it is 4 sheets thick.
Fold it in half again.
After three folds it is 8 sheets thick.

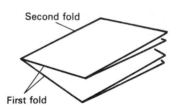

Second fold

First fold

1. Write how many sheets thick it is after:

   (*a*) 4 folds   (*d*) 7 folds

   (*b*) 5 folds   (*e*) 8 folds

   (*c*) 6 folds   (*f*) 9 folds

2. Try to fold the paper in half 7 times then tear it in half.

Using a Calculator

Here are three different ways of finding squares on a calculator. Check which of the methods work on your calculator.

e.g.   To find 5.8^2

Method 1   (Use $5.8^2 = 5.8 \times 5.8$.)

Key in: $\boxed{AC}\ \boxed{5}\ \boxed{\cdot}\ \boxed{8}\ \boxed{\times}\ \boxed{5}\ \boxed{\cdot}\ \boxed{8}\ \boxed{=}$

Method 2

Key in: $\boxed{AC}\ \boxed{5}\ \boxed{\cdot}\ \boxed{8}\ \boxed{\times}\ \boxed{=}$

Method 3   (if the calculator has an $\boxed{x^2}$ key)

Key in: $\boxed{AC}\ \boxed{5}\ \boxed{\cdot}\ \boxed{8}\ \boxed{x^2}$

Exercise 6

Use a calculator to find:

1. 8.7^2	**11.** 6.75^2	**21.** 5.7^2
2. 3.9^2	**12.** 2.86^2	**22.** 57^2
3. 1.8^2	**13.** 9.13^2	**23.** 570^2
4. 4.6^2	**14.** 24.2^2	**24.** 8.2^2
5. 7.3^2	**15.** 81.6^2	**25.** 82^2
6. 24^2	**16.** 1.09^2	**26.** 820^2
7. 92^2	**17.** 365^2	**27.** 734^2
8. 61^2	**18.** 524^2	**28.** 73.4^2
9. 68^2	**19.** 2.71^2	**29.** 7.34^2
10. 53^2	**20.** 44.8^2	**30.** 0.734^2

Number Patterns

Exercise 7

Any number that can be shown as a rectangular pattern of dots is called a *rectangular number*.

12 is a rectangular number: • • • •
　　　　　　　　　　　　　　 • • • •
　　　　　　　　　　　　　　 • • • •

12 can also be shown as: • • • • • •
　　　　　　　　　　　　　 • • • • • •

Note that　• • • •　is the same as　• • •
　　　　　　• • • •　　　　　　　　• • •
　　　　　　• • • •　　　　　　　　• • •
　　　　　　　　　　　　　　　　　• • •

7 is not a rectangular number:　• • • • • • •

A straight line of dots is not called a rectangle.

A Draw dot patterns to show which of these numbers are rectangular numbers:

A. 8	**C.** 5	**E.** 11	**G.** 20	**I.** 28
B. 10	**D.** 18	**F.** 15	**H.** 21	**J.** 9

B Show the number 24 as a rectangular dot pattern in as many different ways as possible.

C **1.** List the first 15 numbers that are not rectangular numbers. (Miss 1, start with 2, 3, 5, 7, and so on.)

2. What are these non-rectangular numbers called? (Choose from: odd, even, prime.)

Exercise 8

Square numbers are numbers that can be shown as a square of dots.

16 is a square number:

We also call the number 1 a square number.

A Show which of these numbers are square numbers by drawing a square pattern of dots. (It may be helpful to use a pegboard.)

A. 4   **B.** 7   **C.** 9   **D.** 18   **E.** 25

B **1.** Write down the first 8 square numbers.

2. What is the tenth square number?

C Copy these then give the next 3 steps:

1. $1 \times 1 = 1$
$2 \times 2 = 4$
$3 \times 3 = 9$
$4 \times 4 = 16$
$5 \times 5 = 25$

2.
$$1 = 1$$
$$1 + 2 + 1 = 4$$
$$1 + 2 + 3 + 2 + 1 = 9$$
$$1 + 2 + 3 + 4 + 3 + 2 + 1 = 16$$

3.
$$1 = 1$$
$$1 + 3 = 4$$
$$1 + 3 + 5 = 9$$
$$1 + 3 + 5 + 7 = 16$$

Copy and complete the multiplication square.

×	1	2	3	4	5	6	7	8	9	10
1	①1			4				8		
2		◯	6						18	
3			◯			18				
4		8		◯						
5				20	◯				45	
6						◯	42			
7			21				◯			70
8	8					48		◯		
9									◯	
10		20						80		◯

What sort of numbers are circled in the main diagonal?

Exercise 10 ———————————————————————

Here are the first five *triangular numbers*:

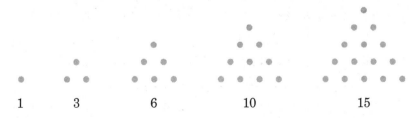

| 1 | 3 | 6 | 10 | 15 |

1. Draw a dot pattern to show the sixth triangular number. What is the sixth triangular number?

2. What is the eighth triangular number? Draw its dot pattern.

3. List the first seventeen triangular numbers. Under each, print O if it is odd and E if it even. The first five of these are shown:

$$1\ 3\ 6\ 10\ 15$$
$$O\ O\ E\ E\ O$$

What do you notice about your answers?

4. Copy this number pattern.
Give the next three rows of the pattern.

$$
\begin{aligned}
1 &= 1 \\
1 + 2 &= 3 \\
1 + 2 + 3 &= 6 \\
1 + 2 + 3 + 4 &= 10 \\
1 + 2 + 3 + 4 + 5 &= 15 \text{ and so on}
\end{aligned}
$$

What sort of numbers are obtained in the answers?

5. Which of these numbers are triangular numbers?
24, 28, 45, 55, 65, 81, 91, 100, 120

Exercise 11

Copy the sequences and fill in the missing numbers:

1. 1, 4, 7, 10, 13, ? , 19, 22, ? , 28

2. 53, 49, 45, 41, ? , 33, 29, 25, ? , 17, 13

3. 5, 15, 25, ? , 45, 55, ? , 75, 85

4. 5, 7, 10, 14, 19, ? , 32, 40, ?

5. 1, 2, 4, 8, 16, ? , 64 ?

6. 1, 2, 1, 4, 1, 6, ? , 8, 1, ?

7. 52, 51, 49, 46, 42, ? , 31, 24, ?

8. 1, 3, 7, 13, 21, 31, ? , 57, 73, ?

9. 1, 4, 9, 16, 25, ? , 49, 64, 81, ?

10. 1, 3, 6, 10, 15, ? , 28, 36, ? , 55, 66

Revision Exercises
XIII to XVIII

Revision Exercise XIII

1. What temperature is shown on the thermometer?

2. Is ⁻30 °C warmer than ⁻20 °C?

3. Write these temperatures in order from coldest to hottest.
   20 °C, ⁻15 °C, 18 °C, ⁻12 °C, ⁻4 °C, 0 °C

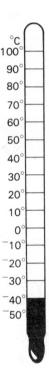

4. For each of these, write whether it is true or false:
   (a) ⁻5 < ⁻2   (b) ⁻2 < 4

5. Copy these, but in place of each question mark write < or > to make each statement correct:
   (a) ⁻7 ⬚ 2   (b) ⁻3 ⬚ ⁻8

6. Mrs Hall had £50 in her bank account. She wrote a cheque for £80. By how much was she then overdrawn?

7. Use the number line on p. 18 to help you to answer these questions:

(a) $3 - 9$ (b) $^-2 + 11$ (c) $^-10 + 8 - 3$

8. It is 8 °C. The temperature falls by 11 °C. What is the new temperature?

9. It is $^-9$ °C. The temperature rises by 2 °C. What is the new temperature?

10. Use the number line on p. 18 to help with these:

(a) $4{\downarrow} + 7{\uparrow}$ (b) $6{\uparrow} + 2{\downarrow}$ (c) $5{\downarrow} + 3{\downarrow} + 2{\uparrow}$

Revision Exercise XIV ═══════════════ M

Copy and complete these mapping diagrams. Answer the questions given.

1.

has the same number of letters as

Two — Two
Three — Three
Five — Five
Six — Six
Seven — Seven

(a) What does five map to?
(b) What maps to three?
(c) What maps to seven?

2.

has the units digit

114
286
34 — 4
509 — 5
16 — 6
125 — 9

(a) What does 125 map to?
(b) What maps to 6?

236

3.

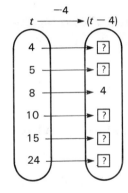

(a) What maps to 11?

(b) What maps to 0?

(c) What does 10 map to?

Revision Exercise XV

A Draw a pair of axes as shown. Use a scale of 1 cm to 1 unit on both axes.

Label the *x*-axis from $^-8$ to $^+8$.

Label the *y*-axis from $^-10$ to $^+10$.

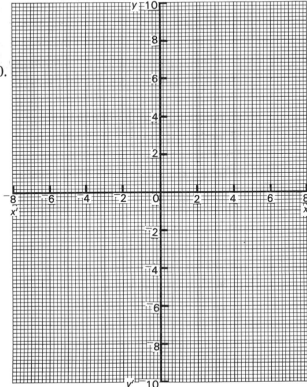

Answer all the following on the same piece of graph paper using the same pair of axes.

1. Plot the points:
   (1, 3), (1, 7), (7, 7) and (7, 3)
   Join them to make a rectangle.
   Draw both diagonals.
   Write the point of intersection of the diagonals.

2. Plot the points:
   ($^-$6, 1), ($^-$4, 6), ($^-$2, 1), ($^-$6, 1)
   and join them in that order.
   What sort of triangle have you drawn?

3. Plot the points:
   ($^-$3, $^-$5), (2, $^-$5), (0, $^-$7), ($^-$5, $^-$7), ($^-$3, $^-$5)
   and join them in that order.
   What is the name of the shape you have drawn?

B 1. Copy and complete the mapping diagram, the pairs of co-ordinates and the table for the relation 'is 1 less than'.

is
x — 1 less than → y

0 → 1	(0, 1)
1 → ?	(1, ?)
2 → ?	(2, ?)
3 → ?	(3, ?)
4 → 5	(4, 5)
5 → ?	(5, ?)
6 → ?	(6, ?)
7 → ?	(7, ?)
8 → 9	(8, 9)

x	y
0	1
1	
2	
3	
4	5
5	
6	
7	
8	9

2. Draw a pair of axes as shown. Use a scale of 2 cm to 1 unit on both axes.

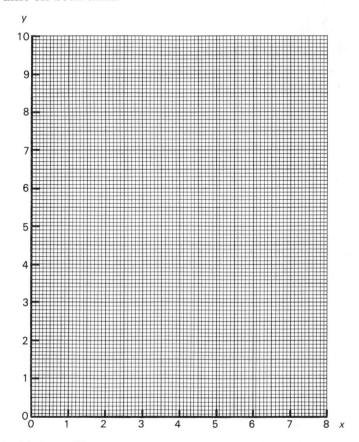

Plot the points found in question 1 on p. 238.

Draw a graph of the relation 'is 1 less than'.

C The table shows how far a car will travel on each litre of petrol:

Number of litres used	0	1	2	3	4	5	6
Number of kilometres travelled	0	15	30			75	90

1. Copy and complete the table.

2. Draw a pair of axes as shown. Use a scale of 2 cm to 1 ℓ on the *horizontal* axis and 1 cm to 5 km on the *vertical* axis.

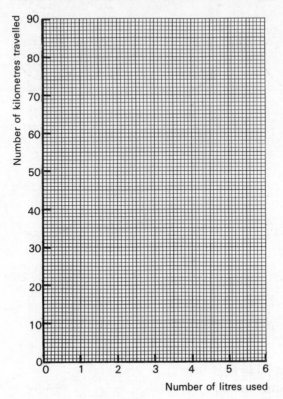

3. Use the table to help you to draw a graph.

Revision Exercise XVI

1. Write the diameter and the radius of this circle:

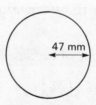

47 mm

2. Find the circumference of each of the following circles:

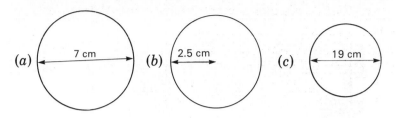

(a) 7 cm (b) 2.5 cm (c) 19 cm

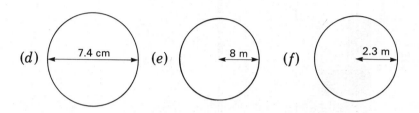

(d) 7.4 cm (e) 8 m (f) 2.3 m

3. Find the circumference of the circle in question 1. Use the formula,

$$\text{Circumference,} \quad C \approx 3d$$

4. How long is a label that fits exactly around a tin of beans, if the tin has a diameter of 74 mm?

Revision Exercise XVII ⬛ M

1. Write whether the transformation is a translation or a rotation:

(a) Folding the arms of a pair of glasses

(b) A pebble falling after being dropped

2. Copy these shapes on to 1 cm squared paper (or graph paper):

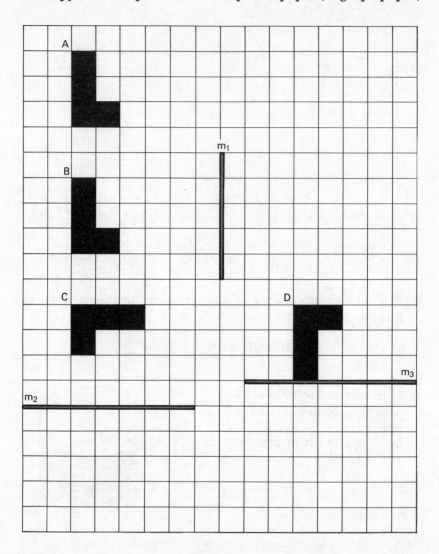

(a) Place your cut out L-shape in position A.
Draw around it. Translate it 5 cm to the right
and draw around it again. Label this new
position T.

(b) Reflect the other L-shapes in the given mirrors.
Draw their images.

3. Start in the given position.
Draw the final position
after a $\frac{1}{4}$ turn anticlockwise.

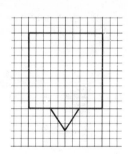

Revision Exercise XVIII

1. Write $u \times u \times u \times u \times u$ in index form.

2. Find the value of:
   (a) 7^2 (b) 2^4 (c) 3^3

3. If $A = l^2$, find A when $l = 20$.

4. If $A = 2l^2$, find A when $l = 4$.

5. Use a calculator to find:
   (a) 5.9^2 (b) 87^2 (c) 2.93^2 (d) 46.1^2

6. Show the number 30 as a rectangular dot pattern in two different ways.

7. Here is a set of numbers: $\{3, 4, 6, 12, 16, 24, 25\}$
   Write the square numbers that are in the above set.

8. Show the triangular number 10 as a dot pattern.

9. Which triangular numbers lie between 20 and 30?

10. Copy the sequences, and fill in the missing numbers:
    (a) 2, 3, 5, 8, 12, $\boxed{?}$, 23, 30, $\boxed{?}$
    (b) 1, 4, 9, 16, $\boxed{?}$, 36, 49, $\boxed{?}$, 81, 100

19 Basic Algebra

Formulae

Exercise 1

1. To change centimetres into millimetres, multiply by 10.
Change to millimetres:
(*a*) 4 cm   (*b*) 7 cm   (*c*) 29 cm

2. To change feet into yards, divide by 3.
Change to yards:
(*a*) 12 ft   (*b*) 27 ft   (*c*) 180 ft

3. To change feet into inches, multiply by 12.
Change to inches:
(*a*) 3 ft   (*b*) 7 ft   (*c*) 32 ft

4. The radius of a circle is half the diameter.
Find the radius if the diameter is:
(*a*) 8 cm   (*b*) 72 mm   (*c*) 3.8 cm

5. To find the perimeter of an equilateral triangle, multiply the
length of one of its sides by 3.
Find the perimeter of an equilateral triangle with sides of:
(*a*) 7 cm   (*b*) 63 mm   (*c*) 8.4 cm

6. The area of a parallelogram is given by the product of its base
and perpendicular height. Find the area of a parallelogram
with base 17 cm and perpendicular height 9 cm.

7. To find the average speed for a journey, divide the distance
travelled by the time taken. Find the average speed of a car
that travels 135 miles in 3 h.

Exercise 2

1.
$$\text{cm} \xrightarrow{\times 10} \text{mm}$$
Change to millimetres:

(*a*) 8 cm   (*b*) 14 cm   (*c*) 31 cm

2.
$$\text{mm} \xrightarrow{\div 10} \text{cm}$$
Change to centimetres:

(*a*) 50 mm   (*b*) 90 mm   (*c*) 470 mm

3.
$$\text{ft} \xrightarrow{\div 3} \text{yd}$$
Change to yards:

(*a*) 15 ft   (*b*) 24 ft   (*c*) 210 ft

4.
$$\text{yd} \xrightarrow{\times 3} \text{ft}$$
Change to feet:

(*a*) 3 yd   (*b*) 11 yd   (*c*) 17 yd

5.
$$\text{ft} \xrightarrow{\times 12} \text{in}$$
Change to inches:

(*a*) 4 ft   (*b*) 6 ft   (*c*) 27 ft

6.
$$\text{in} \xrightarrow{\div 12} \text{ft}$$
Change to feet:

(*a*) 24 in   (*b*) 60 in   (*c*) 96 in

7.
$$\text{Diameter} \xrightarrow{\div 2} \text{Radius}$$

Find the radius of a circle if the diameter is:

(*a*) 12 cm   (*b*) 38 mm   (*c*) 5.4 m

8. Radius $\xrightarrow{\times 2}$ Diameter

Find the diameter of a circle if the radius is:

(*a*) 3 cm   (*b*) 44 mm   (*c*) 7.6 m

9. Length of side $\xrightarrow{\times 3}$ Perimeter

Find the perimeter of an equilateral triangle where the sides are:

(*a*) 12 cm   (*b*) 15 m   (*c*) 2.6 m

10. Perimeter $\xrightarrow{\div 3}$ Length of side

Find the length of each side of an equilateral triangle with perimeter:

(*a*) 18 cm   (*b*) 30 cm   (*c*) 42 mm

Exercise 3

1. The formula $P = 4l$ can be used to find the perimeter of a square. Find P when $l = 6$.

2. Angles on a straight line add up to 180°.
The formula $B = 180 - A$ can be used to find one angle when the other is given. Find angle B when angle $A = 65°$.

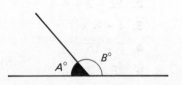

3. $A = lb$ gives the area of a rectangle. Find A when $l = 7$ and $b = 3$.

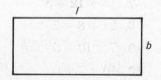

4. The formula $s = vt$ gives the distance travelled s in a time t. v is how fast you travel.
Find s when $v = 80$ and $t = 3$.

5. $R = \dfrac{V}{I}$ is a formula used in science. It has something to do with electricity. It comes from Ohm's law.
Find R when $V = 240$ and $I = 5$.

6. $d = 2r$ gives the diameter of a circle when the radius r is known. Find d when $r = 26$.

7. $C = \pi d$ gives the circumference of a circle. d is the diameter. π is a Greek letter called 'pi'. π is roughly 3.
Find C if $\pi = 3$ and $d = 17$.

Exercise 4   Order of Precedence

Find the value of:

e.g. 1 $5 \times 4 + 6$
$= 20 + 6$
$= \underline{\underline{26}}$

e.g. 2 $3 + 6 \times 4$
$= 3 + 24$
$= \underline{\underline{27}}$

1. $4 \times 5 + 3$

2. $12 \div 2 + 4$

3. $4 + 6 \times 7$

4. $5 + 15 \div 5$

5. $19 - 2 \times 3$

6. $3 \times 6 + 2$

7. $15 + 12 \div 3$

8. $24 \div 8 - 2$

9. $7 \times 10 - 5$

10. $10 + 7 \times 6$

11. $9 \times 5 - 8$

12. $20 \div 4 - 2$

13. $30 - 18 \div 6$

14. $8 \times 6 - 8$

15. $8 + 10 \div 2$

16. $36 \div 4 - 5$

17. $8 \times 10 - 9$

18. $4 \times 9 + 12$

19. $40 - 8 \div 2$

20. $50 - 4 \times 9$

Exercise 5   Substitution

If $p = 3$, $q = 5$, $t = 2$ and $u = 12$, find the value of:

1. $p + q$	**9.** pq	**17.** $p + qt$
2. $t + p$	**10.** uq	**18.** $qt + p$
3. $u + q$	**11.** $\frac{u}{t}$	**19.** $u - qt$
4. $q + u$	**12.** $pq + t$	**20.** $p + tu$
5. $u - t$	**13.** $tq - p$	**21.** $u - pt$
6. pt	**14.** $u \div p + q$	**22.** $t + pq$
7. ut	**15.** $u \div t - p$	**23.** $t + qp$
8. $u \div p$	**16.** $ut + q$	**24.** $u + qu$

Exercise 6   Operations

e.g. 1   If $a * b$ means $a \times b$, find the value of $7 * 3$.

$$7 * 3 = 7 \times 3$$

$$= \underline{\underline{21}}$$

e.g. 2   If $x * y$ means $2x + y$, find the value of $4 * 9$.

$$4 * 9 = 2 \times 4 + 9$$

$$= 8 + 9$$

$$= \underline{\underline{17}}$$

1. If $p * q$ means $p - q$, find the value of:
   (a) $7 * 3$ (b) $12 * 4$ (c) $26 * 12$

2. If $l * m$ means $2l - m$, find the value of:
   (a) $4 * 3$ (b) $9 * 6$ (c) $15 * 10$

3. If $a * c$ means $a + 2c$, find the value of:
   (a) $7 * 4$ (b) $8 * 9$ (c) $14 * 10$

4. If $u * d$ means $d - u$, find the value of:
   (a) $2 * 9$ (b) $5 * 21$ (c) $13 * 40$

5. If $m * n$ means $2n - m$, find the value of:

    (a) $5 * 7$ (b) $6 * 6$ (c) $3 * 9$

6. If $k * v$ means $\dfrac{(k + v)}{2}$, find the value of:

    (a) $6 * 8$ (b) $9 * 13$ (c) $18 * 24$

Exercise 7   Like Terms

Simplify:

1. $c + c + d + c + d + c + c + d + d$

2. $4m + 2m$

3. $2k + 6k + 5k$

4. $3e + 5f + 2e + 4f$

5. $10b - 2b$

6. $14a - 5a$

7. $9t + 4t - 3t - 7t$

8. $6g - 2g + 5g + 3g - 4g$

9. $2p + p + 4p - 3p - p + 5p$

10. $3x + 2x - x + 5x - 4x - 2x$

11. $2h + 5l - 2l + l + 3h - h$

12. $7u - 2u + 3w - 2w - 3u + 6w$

13. $6z + y - 3z - 2z + 4y - 3y$

14. $4v + 7 - 2v + 6 - 3 + 3v - 1$

15. $5q + 6r - 2q - 3r + 4r - 3q$

16. $3k + 2l - k - l + 4k$

17. $7t - t + 4u - 2t + 5u - 6u$

18. $8p + 7m + 3p - 4m - 5p - 2p$

19. $5y + 7z - 2z + 3y - 3y + 2z$

20. $9g + 6h + 4g - 4g - 2h + 2h$

249

Exercise 8

Write the following in a shorter form and simplify your answers:

e.g. Alan had collected $23c$ conkers. He collected $8c$ more, lost $14c$, gave $9c$ away, then collected a further $11c$. How many conkers would he now have?

He would have $23c + 8c - 14c - 9c + 11c$ conkers

$$= \underline{\underline{19c \text{ conkers}}}$$

1. David had $5m$ marbles. On Monday, he won $7m$, on Tuesday he won $4m$, on Wednesday he lost $6m$ and on Thursday he won $3m$. How many marbles has David now got?

2. Janet won $14p$ house points on Monday, $8p$ on Tuesday, $12p$ on Wednesday, $15p$ on Thursday, and $3p$ on Friday. What was her total for the week?

3. Ketan had $8j$ jelly babies. He ate $3j$, bought $14j$, then ate $9j$. How many did he have left?

4. Richard had $18x$ pence. He spent $5x$ pence on sweets then spent a further $9x$ pence on comics. If he was then given $13x$ pence, how much money would he now have?

5. Mrs Pearson had $4y$ eggs. She bought $15y$ more then used $9y$ on Saturday while baking. $3y$ eggs were used on Sunday for breakfast and $6y$ eggs were bought on Monday. How many eggs does Mrs Pearson now have?

6. At Christmas time I had $37t$ stamps. I used $25t$ of these to post some Christmas cards. I bought $19t$ more, then used another $21t$. How many stamps did I have left?

Exercise 9

1. Ann won $12p$ housepoints on Monday, $7p$ housepoints on Tuesday, $9p$ on Wednesday and $8p$ on Thursday, but she lost $6p$ housepoints on Friday.

   (a) What was her total of housepoints for the week?
   (b) Find her total when $p = 2$.

2. I bought $5h$ sheets of paper. I used h of these, bought $8h$ then used $9h$ more.

   (a) How many have I left?
   (b) How many have I left if $h = 8$?

3. Stephen had $9m$ marbles. He won $7m$ more, lost $5m$, won $6m$, bought $3m$ then lost $13m$.

   (a) How many has he now got?
   (b) How many has he now got if $m = 4$?

4. Sareeta had $8z$ pence. She spent $3z$ pence on a magazine; she was given $7z$ pence; she earned $6z$ pence then spent $12z$ pence on a present for her mum.

   (a) How much money has she left?
   (b) How much money would she have left if $z = 9$?

5. James took $14c$ conkers and $19m$ marbles to school. He gave $11m$ marbles away, lost $8c$ conkers, but was given $3c$ conkers.

   (a) Write, in a short form, the number of things he had left
   (b) If $m = 7$ and $c = 5$, how many marbles did he have left?
   (c) If $m = 7$ and $c = 5$, how many conkers did he have left?

Simplifying Terms

Reminder

$$3 \text{ lots of } 5 = 15$$

that is, $\qquad 3 \times 5 = 15$

Also, 3 lots of 5 apples = 15 apples

that is, $\qquad 3 \times 5 \text{ apples} = 15 \text{ apples}$

Also, $\qquad 3 \text{ lots of } 5a = 15a$

that is, $\qquad 3 \times 5a = 15a$

Exercise 10

e.g. $\quad 3 \times 5a = \underline{\underline{15a}}$

1. $2 \times 4t$
2. $5 \times 6b$
3. $4 \times 6a$
4. $3 \times 4w$
5. $2 \times 5m$
6. $6 \times 3h$
7. $3 \times 9z$
8. $4 \times 9q$
9. $4 \times 7g$
10. $7 \times 4z$

11. $5 \times 3q$
12. $6 \times 4x$
13. $10 \times 5e$
14. $8 \times 3n$
15. $5 \times 9w$
16. $5 \times 8u$
17. $7 \times 7y$
18. $8 \times 4v$
19. $5 \times 7m$
20. $2 \times 10p$

21. $10 \times 9k$
22. $9 \times 7l$
23. $8 \times 8d$
24. $9 \times 6f$
25. $6 \times 7b$
26. $7 \times 6d$
27. $7 \times 8h$
28. $8 \times 7e$
29. $8 \times 9c$
30. $9 \times 8g$

20 Statistics

Exercise 1

1. The table shows the number of ice lollies sold each day by a shop.

Draw a pictogram from the table:

Day of the week	Mon	Tues	Wed	Thurs	Fri	Sat
Number of ice lollies sold	12	6	10	17	15	18

Do not forget to give a title.
Do not forget to give a key.

2. Draw a bar chart to show the number of newspapers delivered each day:

Newspaper	Number delivered
Chronicle	8
Courier	15
Gazette	18
Herald	6
Daily News	19
Daily Post	12

Use a scale of 1 cm to 1 newspaper.

1. (*a*) Copy this tally chart:

Vowel	Tally	Frequency
a		
e		
i		
o		
u		

(*b*) Complete the tally chart by marking a tally mark for each vowel in the first seven lines of text on p. 122 starting at 'For thousands of'.

(*c*) Draw a bar chart to show the number of vowels. Use a scale of 2 cm for 5 on the frequency axis.

2. (*a*) Draw a tally chart to show the times taken to count to 50 in fives (5, 10, 15, 20 and so on). Time each person in your class. Use a stopwatch. Find the times to the nearest second.

Time (s)	Tally	Frequency
2		
3		
4		
5		

(*b*) Draw a bar chart from your tally chart.

Jagged Line Graphs

Exercise 3

In hospitals, jagged line graphs are drawn for each patient. The graph shows temperature, pulse rate and respiration. The readings for the graphs shown were taken every 4 h.

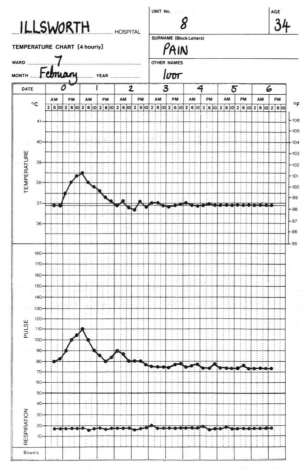

Answer these questions using the graphs:

1. On which day (0, 1, 2, 3, 4, 5 or 6) and at what time was the temperature highest?

2. What was the highest temperature (in °C)?

3. What was the highest pulse rate?

4. What was the pulse rate on day 1 at 6 p.m.?

5. What was the temperature on day 2 at 2 p.m.?

6. What was the temperature at 6 p.m. on day 0?

7. What is 'normal' temperature?

8. What is 'normal' rate of respiration?

Exercise 4

1. Draw a jagged line graph to show the car sales each quarter (3 months) for two years.
Use a scale of 2 cm to 5 cars on the *vertical* axis.

Quarter	Year 1				Year 2			
	1st	2nd	3rd	4th	1st	2nd	3rd	4th
Number of cars sold	25	15	35	20	26	10	38	21

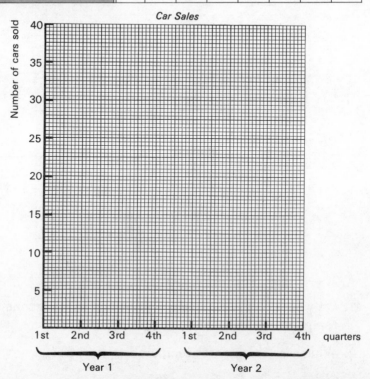

2. Find the daily school attendance for pupils in your class. (Find the *data* for about 10 days.) Draw a jagged line graph of school attendance.

3. Find the temperature in your classroom or outdoors (or home) at the same time each day throughout a week. Draw a jagged line graph of temperatures.

Measuring Angles

Exercise 5

Measure these angles:

1.

3.

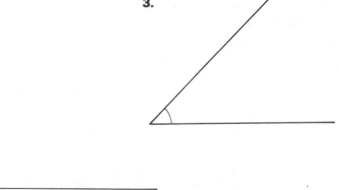

2.

4.

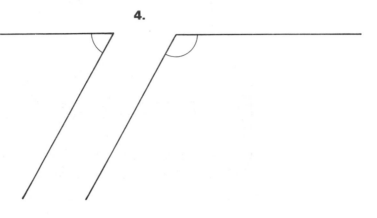

5. **6.**

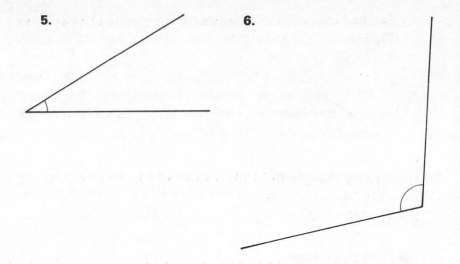

Pie Charts

Exercise 6

1. Here is a drawing of a pie. Bob gets $\frac{1}{4}$ of the pie.
   (a) What fraction does So-So get?
   (b) What fraction does Colin get?

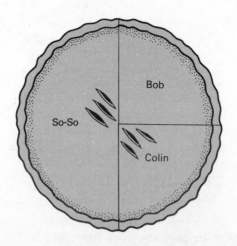

2. Draw a pie of your own. Share it amongst four people so that
   Emma gets $\frac{1}{2}$, Kevin gets $\frac{1}{4}$, Tony and Lenka each get $\frac{1}{8}$.

3. Here is another circle. This time it is not a pie. It is called a *pie chart*.

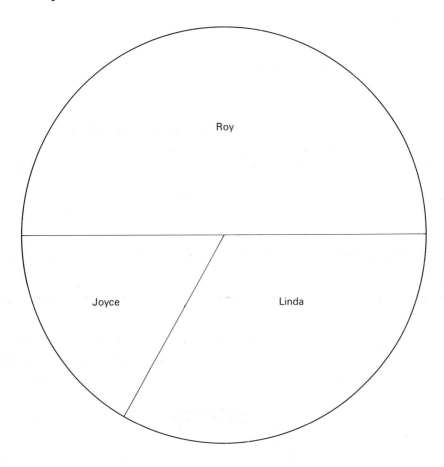

The pie chart shows how 30 sweets are shared amongst 3 people.

There are 360° in a full turn. The circle stands for 30 sweets.

(*a*) Since 360° stands for 30 sweets,

          180° stands for 15 sweets,

           60° stands for 5 sweets,

        120° stands for [?] sweets.

(*b*) How many sweets does Roy get?

(*c*) How many sweets does Joyce get?

(*d*) How many sweets does Linda get?

Exercise 7

1. 12 people were asked which fruit juice they liked best. Their answers are shown in the pie chart.

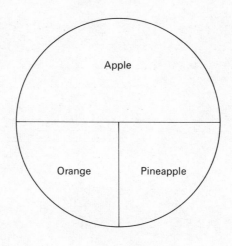

Fruit juice liked

(*a*) What fraction liked apple juice?

(*b*) How many liked apple juice?

(*c*) What fraction liked orange juice?

(*d*) How many degrees stand for orange juice?

(*e*) How many liked orange juice?

(*f*) How many liked pineapple juice?

(*g*) Since 360° stands for 12 people,
            180° stands for ? people,
             90° stands for ? people.

2. The pie chart shows the school clubs attended by 36 pupils on a certain day.

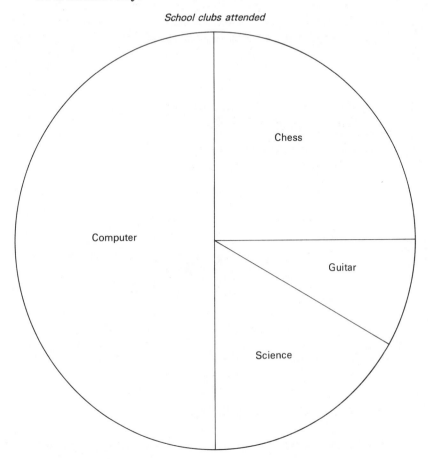

School clubs attended

(*a*) Copy the pie chart.

(*b*) Copy and complete: 360° stands for 36 people,
                           180° stands for ? people,
                            90° stands for 9 people,
                            30° stands for ? people,
       and   60° stands for ? people.

Write how many people attended:

(*c*) The computer club.

(*d*) The chess club.

(*e*) The science club.

(*f*) The guitar club.

3. 48 people were asked what type of heating they had at home. Here are the results:

Coal	12
Electric	6
Gas	24
Oil	6

(a) Work out the missing numbers:
Since 48 people take up 360°

24 people take up $\boxed{?}$ °

12 people take up $\boxed{?}$ °

and   6 people take up $\boxed{?}$ °

(b) Make out a table using the figures above:

Number of people	Number of degrees
48	360°
24	
12	
6	

(c) Draw a pie chart to show the different types of heating.

Probability

Exercise 8

1. I tossed a coin four times.
The *outcome* was heads, heads, heads, $\boxed{?}$.
What do you think the fourth outcome was, heads or tails?

2. Are you certain that your answer to question 1 is correct?

3. Try an experiment.
Toss a coin 100 times.
Collect your results in a tally chart:

Tossing a Coin

Outcome	Tally	Frequency
Head		
Tail		

4. Draw a bar chart to show your results.

5. Write a sentence about your results.

6. Total the number of heads obtained by the whole class.
Total the number of tails.

7. Draw a bar chart of the class's results.

8. Write a sentence about the class's results.

Exercise 9

1. For some dice games you need to throw a
six to start.

Sylvia and Tue play a game.
Tue said that he would throw
a two to start and not a six.
Sylvia tried to throw a six.

Who is likely to start playing first?

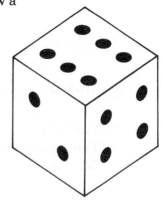

2. Which number on a die is easiest
to throw?

3. Try this experiment.

   (a) Copy this tally chart first:

Number on the die	Tally	Frequency
1		
2		
3		
4		
5		
6		

   (b) Throw a die about 120 times.
   Show your results on the tally chart.

   (c) Draw a bar chart of your results.

   (d) Which number turned up the most?

4. (a) Copy the given frequency table:

   (b) Collect the results of the 'throwing a die' experiment from everyone in your class. Enter the totals for each number in your frequency table.

   (c) Draw a bar chart of the class's results.

   (d) Which number turned up the most for the whole class.

   (e) Does it matter which number you need to start a game?

Throwing a Die

Number on the die	Frequency
1	
2	
3	
4	
5	
6	

5. (*a*) Draw a hexagon on card.
   Make a spinner out of it as shown.

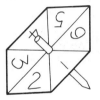

(*b*) Answer question 3 again, but this time use the spinner instead of the die.

(*c*) Answer question 4 for the spinner.

Exercise 10

1. Make several copies of this flag. Colour the two parts of each flag as follows. (Each flag should be different.)

(*a*) Using only two colours to colour the two parts of the flag, two different flags can be made:

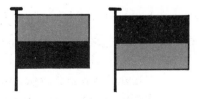

Colour two of your flags using exactly two colours.

(*b*) Choose only three different colours.
   Colour some more copies of the flag. Use two of the three colours at a time, make as many different flags as you can.

(*c*) Choose only four different colours.
   Colour some more copies of the flag. Use two of the four colours at a time, make as many different flags as you can.

2. Make several copies of this flag:

Use exactly three different colours to colour the three parts of the flag. How many different flags can be made?

3. (*a*) Using the digits 2 and 7 once only in each number, make as many different 2-digit numbers as you can.

(*b*) Using the digits 3, 6 and 8 once only in each number, make as many different 2-digit numbers as you can.

(*c*) Using the digits 4, 5, 7 and 9 once only in each number, make as many different 2-digit numbers as you can.

4. Using the digits 2, 5 and 8 once in each number, make as many different 3-digit numbers as you can.

21 Simple Equations

Exercise 1

Find the value of:

1. $5 - 5$
2. $3 - 3$
3. $9 - 9$
4. $2 - 2$
5. $14 - 14$
6. $24 - 24$
7. $47 - 47$
8. $89 - 89$

9. $7 + 5 - 5$
10. $9 + 6 - 6$
11. $12 + 8 - 8$
12. $19 + 14 - 14$
13. $28 + 32 - 32$
14. $73 + 29 - 29$
15. $46 + 87 - 87$
16. $57 + 95 - 95$

17. $8 - 3 + 3$
18. $7 - 4 + 4$
19. $19 - 7 + 7$
20. $26 - 11 + 11$
21. $31 - 19 + 19$
22. $42 - 25 + 25$
23. $64 - 46 + 46$
24. $93 - 58 + 58$

Exercise 2

Simplify:

1. $x + 5 - 5$
2. $n + 7 - 7$
3. $y + 12 - 12$
4. $2d + 8 - 8$
5. $4m + 11 - 11$
6. $3 + t - 3$
7. $2 + g - 2$
8. $9 + k - 9$
9. $4 + 3h - 4$
10. $10 + 2n - 10$

11. $a - 1 + 1$
12. $c - 6 + 6$
13. $z - 8 + 8$
14. $p - 14 + 14$
15. $l - 20 + 20$
16. $2q - 15 + 15$
17. $5r + 13 - 13$
18. $4w - 13 + 13$
19. $6u + 25 - 25$
20. $3v - 25 + 25$

Exercise 3

Copy and complete:

1. $n + 7 - \boxed{?} = n$ 11. $t - 8 + \boxed{?} = t$

2. $k + 3 - \boxed{?} = k$ 12. $w - 2 + \boxed{?} = w$

3. $u + 4 - \boxed{?} = u$ 13. $a - 12 + \boxed{?} = a$

4. $x + 9 - \boxed{?} = x$ 14. $z - 15 + \boxed{?} = z$

5. $3y + 6 - \boxed{?} = 3y$ 15. $h - 20 + \boxed{?} = h$

6. $2t + 10 - \boxed{?} = 2t$ 16. $2b - 1 + \boxed{?} = 2b$

7. $5 + h - \boxed{?} = h$ 17. $4d - 6 + \boxed{?} = 4d$

8. $8 + m - \boxed{?} = m$ 18. $3p + 13 - \boxed{?} = 3p$

9. $11 + k - \boxed{?} = k$ 19. $3p - 13 + \boxed{?} = 3p$

10. $10 + 2c - \boxed{?} = 2c$ 20. $5v - 21 + \boxed{?} = 5v$

Exercise 4   M

e.g. $u + 6 \xrightarrow{\quad -6 \quad} u$

Copy and complete:

1. $c + 2 \xrightarrow{\boxed{?}} c$ 9. $w - 5 \xrightarrow{\boxed{?}} w$

2. $y + 8 \xrightarrow{\boxed{?}} y$ 10. $n - 1 \xrightarrow{\boxed{?}} n$

3. $a + 5 \xrightarrow{\boxed{?}} a$ 11. $q - 7 \xrightarrow{\boxed{?}} q$

4. $p + 12 \xrightarrow{\boxed{?}} p$ 12. $b - 9 \xrightarrow{\boxed{?}} b$

5. $x + 15 \xrightarrow{\boxed{?}} x$ 13. $z - 10 \xrightarrow{\boxed{?}} z$

6. $7 + g \xrightarrow{\boxed{?}} g$ 14. $h - 6 \xrightarrow{\boxed{?}} h$

7. $4 + m \xrightarrow{\boxed{?}} m$ 15. $e - 14 \xrightarrow{\boxed{?}} e$

8. $10 + d \xrightarrow{\boxed{?}} d$ 16. $t - 25 \xrightarrow{\boxed{?}} t$

Here is a balance.
A bag of jelly babies and 3 jelly babies on one pan are balanced by 7 jelly babies on the other pan.

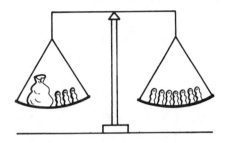

We can write this as a simple equation: $n + 3 = 7$

(Note that n stands for the number of jelly babies in the bag.)

If we take 3 jelly babies off one pan, the balance tips:

1. What should we do to balance the scales again?
(Do not put the 3 jelly babies back on the pan.)

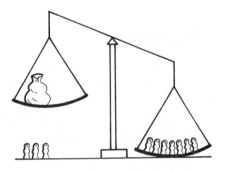

2. How many jelly babies are on the right-hand pan after the scales have balanced again?

3. How many jelly babies must there be in the bag?

The equation shown on the balance can be solved like this:

$n + 3 \quad = 7$

$n + 3 - 3 = 7 - 3$ (3 jelly babies are taken off each side.)

$\therefore \quad \underline{\underline{n \quad = 4}}$

Exercise 6

Solve these equations:

e.g. 1 $x + 5 = 8$

$x + 5 - 5 = 8 - 5$

$\therefore x = 3$

e.g. 2 $d - 3 = 7$

$d - 3 + 3 = 7 + 3$

$\therefore d = 10$

1. $t + 4 = 6$
2. $p + 7 = 12$
3. $u + 2 = 10$
4. $c - 1 = 9$
5. $m - 6 = 10$
6. $y + 8 = 11$
7. $g - 6 = 2$
8. $v - 10 = 10$

9. $k + 10 = 16$
10. $e - 7 = 4$
11. $a + 5 = 14$
12. $f + 9 = 15$
13. $h - 5 = 8$
14. $q + 6 = 20$
15. $b - 14 = 2$
16. $w - 14 = 16$

17. $l + 11 = 12$
18. $z + 11 = 20$
19. $n - 8 = 14$
20. $d + 15 = 25$
21. $x - 12 = 5$
22. $u - 16 = 13$
23. $e + 12 = 12$
24. $s + 20 = 59$

Exercise 7

1. Does $x + 4 = 11$ when $x = 7$?

2. Does $c + 8 = 12$ when $c = 4$?

3. Does $m + 7 = 13$ when $m = 6$?

4. Does $a + 3 = 6$ when $a = 9$?

5. Does $t - 3 = 6$ when $t = 9$?

6. Does $k + 9 = 14$ when $k = 23$?

7. Does $z - 8 = 9$ when $z = 17$?

8. Does $p - 2 = 9$ when $p = 7$?

9. Does $n - 4 = 11$ when $n = 7$?

10. Does $b + 5 = 15$ when $b = 20$?

11. Does $f + 10 = 26$ when $f = 16$?

12. Does $l - 6 = 6$ when $l = 12$?

13. Does $s + 12 = 16$ when $s = 4$?

14. Does $d - 12 = 16$ when $d = 4$?

15. Does $h - 9 = 9$ when $h = 0$?

16. Does $q + 15 = 15$ when $q = 0$?

17. Does $e - 14 = 9$ when $e = 23$?

18. Does $w + 18 = 25$ when $w = 7$?

19. Does $g + 23 = 41$ when $g = 19$?

20. Does $u - 20 = 30$ when $u = 50$?

Exercise 8

1. Does $2p = 12$ when $p = 8$?

2. Does $3a = 30$ when $a = 10$?

3. Does $5u = 45$ when $u = 7$?

4. Does $4d = 32$ when $d = 8$?

5. Does $10x = 60$ when $x = 3$?

6. Does $8t = 48$ when $t = 6$?

7. Does $6m = 30$ when $m = 6$?

8. Does $9k = 63$ when $k = 8$?

9. Does $2f = 36$ when $f = 18$?

10. Does $7w = 63$ when $w = 9$?

Exercise 9

Solve these equations:

1. $2x = 14$	**5.** $2e = 24$	**9.** $4n = 28$	**13.** $7s = 49$
2. $4h = 12$	**6.** $8q = 56$	**10.** $3v = 36$	**14.** $8z = 72$
3. $5v = 30$	**7.** $6x = 46$	**11.** $9c = 36$	**15.** $2a = 46$
4. $7b = 28$	**8.** $7l = 70$	**12.** $5g = 45$	**16.** $3y = 45$

22 Length, Capacity and Mass

It is useful to be able to estimate lengths. Use measurements you know to help you. For small lengths, think how many 1 cm lines will fit. For slightly longer lengths, think how many 1 m lines would fit. You can even think how many men (or women), car lengths or bus lengths would fit if you learn and remember such lengths.

Length

Exercise 1

1. Draw a straight line 1 cm long.

2. Estimate the following lengths. (Try to picture how many of your 1 cm lines would fit.)
   (a) The length and breadth of the cover of this book.
   (b) The length and breadth of a page of your exercise book.
   (c) Any other small lengths.

3. Measure the lengths estimated in question 2.

4. How many centimetres long is your ruler?

5. Estimate the following lengths. (Try to picture how many rulers would fit.)
   (a) The length of your desk.
   (b) The length of a dining table.
   (c) Any other lengths you think are several rulers long.

6. Measure the lengths estimated in question 5.

Exercise 2

1. Draw a straight line 1 m long (draw it on the blackboard or on the playground) or look at a metre ruler or tape.

2. Estimate these distances. (Try to picture how many of your 1-metre lines would fit.)
   (a) The length of your classroom.
   (b) The breadth of your classroom.
   (c) Other distances that are several metres long.

3. Measure the distances estimated in question 2.

Exercise 3

1. Mark a short line on the playground.
   Walk ten paces starting at that line.
   Mark the place where the tenth pace ends.
   Measure the distance walked.
   Divide the distance by 10 to find the length of one pace.

2. Walk across the playground and count your paces. Now work out the distance across the playground.

3. By counting paces, find other distances.

4. Use a tape measure to check the distances in question 3 and the distance across the playground.

Exercise 4

1. Draw chalk marks on the playground every half metre for a distance of 5 m.

2. Practise walking $\frac{1}{2}$-metre paces. Use the chalk marks to help.

3. Try this competition:
   Mark a starting line. Everyone should walk in a straight line from the starting line and try to pace out 50 m (or 25 m if 50 m is too far). Several people can walk at the same time. Each person's stopping point should be marked on the ground. By measuring, find out who in the class was closest to 50 m (or 25 m).

Exercise 5

1. How long is a normal-sized paperclip?
   A. 25 mm
   B. 50 mm
   C. 75 mm
   D. 100 mm

2. How long is a teaspoon?
   A. 12 cm
   B. 20 cm
   C. 250 mm
   D. 1.5 m

3. What would be about 2 m high?
   A. A chair seat
   B. A door
   C. A house
   D. A church tower

4. What would be about 1.2 m long?
   A. A bath towel
   B. A knife
   C. A car
   D. A bus

5. How high is a room?
   A. 4.3 m
   B. 2.4 m
   C. 1.6 m
   D. 110 mm

6. How long is a shoe?
   A. 25 cm
   B. 45 cm
   C. 65 cm
   D. 85 cm

7. What is the height of a table (or desk)?
   A. 50 cm
   B. 73 cm
   C. 1 m
   D. 1.5 m

8. How long is a matchstick?
   A. 23 mm
   B. 46 mm
   C. 72 mm
   D. 100 mm

9. How long is a tennis court?
   A. 12 m
   B. 24 m
   C. 48 m
   D. 60 m

10. How long is a soccer pitch?
    A. 25 m
    B. 50 m
    C. 100 m
    D. 150 m

Exercise 6

Copy this table of length:

$$10 \text{ mm} = 1 \text{ cm}$$
$$100 \text{ cm} = 1 \text{ m}$$
$$1000 \text{ mm} = 1 \text{ m}$$
$$1000 \text{ m} = 1 \text{ km}$$

Try to learn this table.
We sometimes need to change from one unit of measurement to another. For example, changing from centimetres to millimetres is changing from one unit to another.

Exercise 7

Copy and complete:

1. 4 cm = ⬚ mm

2. 7 cm = ⬚ mm

3. 30 mm = ⬚ cm

4. 90 mm = ⬚ cm

5. 60 mm = ⬚ cm

6. 10 cm = ⬚ mm

7. 2 m = ⬚ cm

8. 6 m = ⬚ cm

9. 300 cm = ⬚ m

10. 800 cm = ⬚ m

11. 2000 mm = ⬚ m

12. 8000 mm = ⬚ m

13. 3 m = ⬚ mm

14. 5 m = ⬚ mm

15. 6 km = ⬚ m

16. 9 km = ⬚ m

17. 4000 m = ⬚ km

18. 6000 m = ⬚ km

19. 4.5 cm = ⬚ mm

20. 2.9 cm = ⬚ mm

21. 58 mm = ⬚ cm

22. 94 mm = ⬚ cm

23. 1800 m = ⬚ km

24. 6.2 km = ⬚ m

Exercise 8

For each question, write L if AB is longer than CD, write S if AB is shorter than CD and write E if AB and CD are of equal length. DO NOT MEASURE.

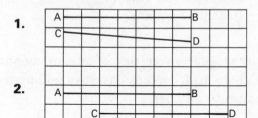

1.

2.

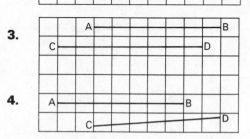

3.

4.

Exercise 9

Calculate the perimeter of each shape:

1.

8 cm

3 cm | Rectangle

2.

7 cm

Square

3.

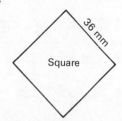

36 mm

Square

4.

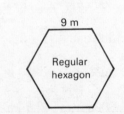

9 m

Regular hexagon

5.

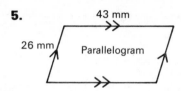

43 mm

26 mm   Parallelogram

6.

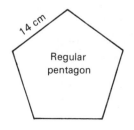

14 cm

Regular
pentagon

7.

8 cm

$5\frac{1}{2}$ cm   Trapezium   7 cm

$13\frac{1}{2}$ cm

8.

19 m

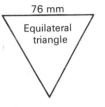

Rhombus

9.

76 mm

Equilateral
triangle

10.

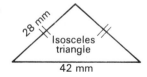

28 mm

Isosceles
triangle

42 mm

11.

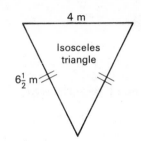

4 m

Isosceles
triangle

$6\frac{1}{2}$ m

12.

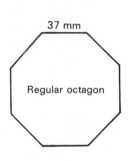

Kite

96 cm   42 cm

13.

37 mm

Regular octagon

14.

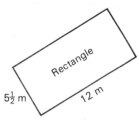

Rectangle

$5\frac{1}{2}$ m   12 m

15.

54 mm

Pentagon

37 mm

48 mm

277

Exercise 10

1. Find the perimeter of a square of side 6 cm.

2. Find the perimeter of a rectangle of length 8 cm and breadth 5 cm.

3. A field is 78 m long and 47 m wide. Find its perimeter.

4. A square has a perimeter of 28 cm. Find the length of each side.

5. Perimeter of the rectangle = 60 mm
   Breadth = 12 mm
   Length = [?]

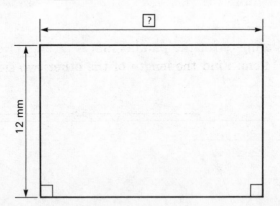

6. The perimeter of a kite is 240 mm. If each of the longer sides is 70 mm long, find the length of the short sides.

7. A rhombus has a perimeter of 92 mm. Find the length of each side.

8. An equilateral triangle has a perimeter of 54 mm. Find the length of each side.

9. Perimeter of this isoceles triangle = 36 m
Third side = ?

10. One side of an isoceles triangle measures 34 mm. The other two sides are twice as long. Find the perimeter of the isoceles triangle.

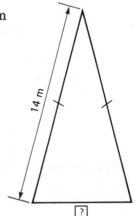

11. The shortest side of an isoceles triangle is 15 cm. If its perimeter is 49 cm, find the length of the two long sides.

12. The perimeter of the parallogram is 80 cm. Two sides are each 14 cm. Find the length of the other two sides.

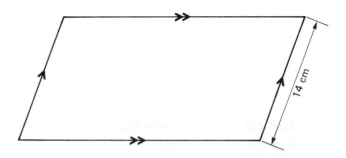

13. The perimeter of a regular hexagon is 138 mm. Find the length of each side.

14. The breadth of a rectangle is 7 m.
The length is four times as big as the breadth.
Work out the perimeter.

15. The length of a rectangle is twice its breadth. Find its perimeter if its length is 48 cm.

Exercise 11

Royal Lytham and St. Anne's Golf Club

Hole	Length (m)	Par	Hole	Length (m)	Par	Hole	Length (m)	Par
1	188	3	7	504	5	13	310	4
2	384	4	8	360	4	14	407	4
3	419	4	9	148	3	15	428	4
4	359	4	10	305	4	16	326	4
5	172	3	11	443	5	17	378	4
6	444	5	12	173	3	18	353	4

1. (*a*) Which is the longest hole?
(*b*) How many metres is it?

2. (*a*) Which is the shortest hole?
(*b*) How many metres is it?

3. How long are the first three holes altogether?

4. How much longer is hole 2 than hole 1?

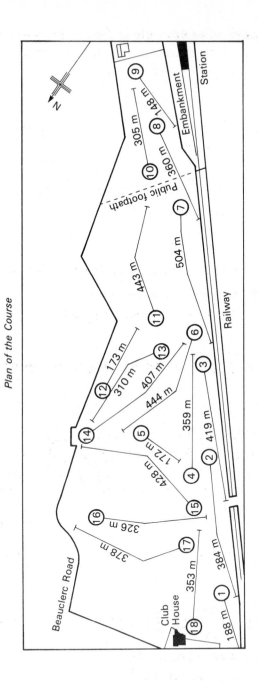

Royal Lytham and St. Anne's Golf Club

Plan of the Course

5. How long are holes 13, 14, 15 and 16 altogether?

6. How long are the first nine holes altogether?

    (*a*) Write the answer in metres.
    (*b*) Write the answer in kilometres.

7. How long are the last nine holes altogether?

    (*a*) Write the answer in metres.
    (*b*) Write the answer in kilometres.

8. A golfer plays one round of golf. How far does that golfer walk altogether? (Give the answer in kilometres.)

Exercise 12

1. Draw a straight line XY, 74 mm long.
Mark a point P on the line such that XP = 36 mm. How long is YP?

2. Draw a straight line AB, 72 mm long.
Bisect AB using a pair of compasses.
Draw the perpendicular bisector.
Mark a point X on the perpendicular bisector such that X lies 15 mm above line AB.
How long is AX?

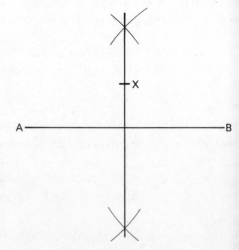

3. Draw a straight line PQ, 112 mm long.
Mark a point C on the line, where PC = 50 mm.
Draw ∠ QCD = 50° and mark point D,
where CD = 47 mm. How long is DQ?

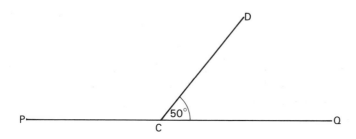

4. Construct an equilateral triangle with sides of 5 cm.

5. Construct an isosceles
triangle LMN, where base
MN = 44 mm and where
the base angles are 65°.
How long is LM?

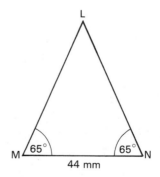

Measurements so far have been in the *metric system.*
The units used are called *metric units.*
Sometimes *imperial units* are used.

Using imperial units of length:

$$
\begin{aligned}
12 \text{ in} &= 1 \text{ ft} \\
3 \text{ ft} &= 1 \text{ yd} \\
1760 \text{ yd} &= 1 \text{ mile}
\end{aligned}
$$

Inches are marked along the edge of the next page.

Exercise 13

1. Dave is 6 ft tall. How many inches is that?

2. Sandra is 5 ft 4 in tall. How many inches is that?

3. I bought 4 yd of material and used 3 yd 1 ft. How many feet were left?

4. A doorway is 2 ft 5 in wide. How many inches is that.

5. I need 24 ft of flex to make a lead for a lamp. How many yards is that?

6. I need 3 pieces of elastic, each 20 in long. How many feet of elastic is that?

Exercise 14

Use imperial units. Measure the lengths of six items (such as a pencil or a pen). If you do not have a suitable ruler nor a tape measure, use the inches marked along the edge of this page.

Capacity

The *capacity* of a container is the amount of liquid it will hold. Small amounts of liquid are usually measured in millilitres (mℓ). Large amounts of liquid are usually measured in litres (ℓ).

$$1000 \text{ m}\ell = 1 \ell$$

Exercise 15

A Change to millilitres:

1. 2 ℓ	**4.** 9 ℓ	**7.** 23 ℓ	**10.** 5.6 ℓ
2. 4 ℓ	**5.** 11 ℓ	**8.** 25 ℓ	**11.** $\frac{1}{2}$ ℓ
3. 7 ℓ	**6.** 15 ℓ	**9.** 7.5 ℓ	**12.** $3\frac{1}{2}$ ℓ

B Change to litres:

1. 3000 ml	**5.** 10 000 ml	**9.** 2500 ml
2. 5000 ml	**6.** 12 000 ml	**10.** 3200 ml
3. 6000 ml	**7.** 17 000 ml	**11.** 5100 ml
4. 8000 ml	**8.** 21 000 ml	**12.** 6800 ml

In the imperial system, gallons (gal) are used for large amounts of liquid and pints (pt) for small amounts:

$$8 \text{ pt} = 1 \text{ gal}$$

Exercise 16

A Change to pints:

1. 2 gal	**3.** 7 gal	**5.** 12 gal	**7.** 15 gal
2. 4 gal	**4.** 9 gal	**6.** 14 gal	**8.** 20 gal

B Change to gallons:

1. 24 pt	**3.** 48 pt	**5.** 80 pt
2. 40 pt	**4.** 64 pt	**6.** 88 pt

Exercise 17

Choose some containers.

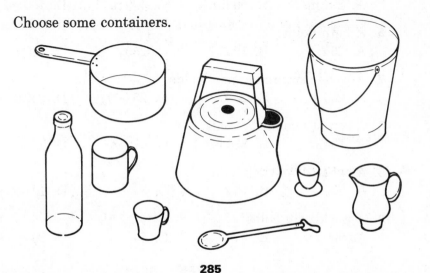

285

Write their names in a list.

Write the capacity of each one in (l) or (ml).

Note: you may need to pour water.

Container	Capacity
Bucket	
Egg cup	
Shampoo bottle	
and so on	

Exercise 18

Choose the answer that is correct or almost correct:

1. A milk bottle holds:

   A. 4 l B. 20 l C. 600 ml D. 20 ml

2. A teaspoonful of medicine is:

   A. 5 ml B. 20 ml C. 100 ml D. 1 l

3. A bucket holds:

   A. 1000 ml B. 9 l C. 24 l D. 600 ml

4. A kettle holds:

   A. 1.7 l B. 3 l C. 6.6 l D. 4000 ml

5. A cup holds:

   A. 200 ml B. 50 ml C. 400 ml D. 100 ml

6. A bath holds:

   A. 85 l B. 12 l C. 250 l D. 110 l

7. A public swimming pool holds:

   A. 250 l B. 2500 l C. 25 000 l D. 250 000 l

8. A can of lemonade holds:

   A. 75 ml B. 330 ml C. 675 ml D. 3.75 l

9. A car's petrol tank holds:

   A. 60 l B. 15 l C. 5 l D. 10 000 ml

10. A washbasin holds:

   A. 950 ml B. 3 l C. 8 l D. 20 l

Exercise 19

Choose the answer that is correct or almost correct:

1. A kettle holds:
    A. 1 gal   B. 3 pt   C. 1 pt   D. $\frac{1}{2}$ pt

2. A tall thin glass holds:
    A. 1 gal   B. 3 pt   C. 1 pt   D. $\frac{1}{2}$ pt

3. A bath holds:
    A. 100 pt   B. 15 gal   C. 35 gal   D. 55 gal

4. A watering can holds:
    A. 2 pt   B. 5 pt   C. 2 gal   D. 5 gal

5. A milk pan holds:
    A. 8 pt   B. 4 pt   C. 2 pt   D. $\frac{1}{2}$ pt

6. A milk bottle holds:
    A. 1 pt   B. 5 pt   C. 10 pt   D. 1 gal

Exercise 20

1. I have four 500 m*l* cartons of milk. How many litres is that?

2. A mug holds 250 m*l*.
    (*a*) How many millilitres will 2 mugs hold?
    (*b*) How many mugs can be filled from 1 *l* of water?

3. How many 200 m*l* cups can be filled from 1 *l* of tea?

4. I filled 10 glasses with milk. Each glass held 300 m*l*. How many litres of milk were there altogether?

5. How many 5 m*l* spoonfuls of medicine can you get from a 100 m*l* bottle?

6. A cow gives 36 *l* of milk each day. How many litres is that in a week?

7. If 1 ℓ of fruit juice fills 3 glasses, how many litres are needed to fill 18 glasses?

8. If a teapot holds 1 ℓ and a kettle holds 1.5 ℓ how many times must the kettle be boiled to fill the teapot 6 times?

Mass

The main metric unit of mass is the *kilogram* (kg). Other units of mass are the gram (g), milligram (mg) and metric tonne (t).

Mass is often wrongly called weight. (Mass is the amount of matter in a body. On Earth, weight is the force with which the body is attracted towards the centre of the Earth.)

$$
\begin{aligned}
1\ t &= 1000\ kg \\
1\ kg &= 1000\ g \\
1\ g &= 1000\ mg
\end{aligned}
$$

Note that 1 ℓ of water has a mass of about 1 kg.

Exercise 21

Copy these but replace the question marks with tonnes (t), kilograms (kg), grams (g) or milligrams (mg) to make each sentence correct:

1. A jar of jam has a mass of 454 | ? | .

2. A teabag has a mass of 3 | ? | .

3. A packet of flour has a mass of 1.5 | ? | .

4. A drawing pin has a mass of 0.5 | ? | .

5. A loaf of bread has a mass of 800 | ? | .

6. A car has a mass of about 1 | ? | .

7. A lorry has a mass of about 10 | ? | .

8. A bar of chocolate has a mass of about 100 | ? | .

Exercise 22

A Collect about ten different things to weigh. Pick up each one. By feel, put them in order from heaviest to lightest. List them in that order. Weigh each one. Write the mass of each object alongside its name.

B Find the mass of about twenty common objects, such as a jar of jam, a tin of fruit, a packet of tea, a bag of potatoes, a suitcase and so on. (On some items the mass may be printed on the label. On a jar of jam the mass given on the label probably does not include the mass of the jar.)

List the objects and their masses or make drawings.

C If you did badly in Exercise 21 then try it again now.

Exercise 23

1. Lift a mass of 1 kg (a bag of sugar probably has a mass of 1 kg). Try to remember what a mass of 1 kg feels like.

2. Make a list of objects that you think weigh about 1 kg.

3. Weigh the objects in question 2 and see if you were nearly right.

Exercise 24

Choose the best answer:

1. An apple has a mass of about:
   A. 130 mg   B. 130 g   C. 500 mg   D. 500 g

2. A marble has a mass of about:
A. 75 mg   B. 200 mg   C. 850 mg   D. 6 g

3. A woman has a mass of about:
A. 25 kg   B. 150 kg   C. 55 kg   D. 940 g

3. A textbook has a mass of about:
A. 540 mg   B. 5.4 g   C. 54 g   D. 540 g

4. A 10 p piece has a mass of about:
A. 113 mg   B. 113 g   C. 1.13 g   D. 11.3 g

6. A new-born baby has a mass of about:
A. 1 kg   B. 3 kg   C. 9 kg   D. 15 kg

7. A 53-seater coach has a mass of about:
A. 7 t   B. 4 t   C. 1 t   D. 870 kg

8. A television set has a mass of about:
A. 25 kg   B. 75 kg   C. 100 kg   D. 140 kg

9. An iron has a mass of about:
A. 1.5 kg   B. 8 kg   C. 280 g   D. 890 mg

10. A cricket ball has a mass of about:
A. 80 g   B. 420 g   C. 160 g   D. 420 mg

Exercise 25

A Change to grams:

1. 4 kg	**4.** 5 kg	**7.** 16 kg	**10.** 5.5 kg
2. 8 kg	**5.** 10 kg	**8.** 24 kg	**11.** 8.5 kg
3. 2 kg	**6.** 12 kg	**9.** 1 kg	**12.** 6.8 kg

B Change to kilograms:

1. 3000 g	**4.** 6000 g	**7.** 11 000 g	**10.** 3500 g
2. 7000 g	**5.** 13 000 g	**8.** 21 000 g	**11.** 1700 g
3. 9000 g	**6.** 15 000 g	**9.** 45 000 g	**12.** 7800 g

Exercise 26

Copy and complete:

1. 9 kg = ? g   **9.** 2 g = ? mg

2. 7 kg = ? g   **10.** 7 g = ? mg

3. 4000 g = ? kg   **11.** 3000 mg = ? g

4. 14 000 g = ? kg   **12.** 5000 mg = ? g

5. 18 kg = ? g   **13.** 2.5 kg = ? g

6. 25 kg = ? g   **14.** 6500 g = ? kg

7. 20 kg = ? g   **15.** 3900 g = ? kg

8. 32 000 g = ? kg   **16.** 4.9 kg = ? g

The main units of mass in the imperial system are ounces (oz), pounds (lb), stones (st), hundredweights (cwt) and tons:

$$
\begin{aligned}
16\ \text{oz} &= 1\ \text{lb} \\
14\ \text{lb} &= 1\ \text{st} \\
112\ \text{lb} &= 1\ \text{cwt} \\
8\ \text{st} &= 1\ \text{cwt} \\
20\ \text{cwt} &= 1\ \text{ton}
\end{aligned}
$$

Exercise 27

1. A cake recipe uses 8 oz flour. How many pounds of flour are needed to make 6 cakes?

2. Another recipe uses 4 oz butter. I have 1 lb butter and make 3 cakes. How many ounces are left?

3. June has a mass of 6 st. How many pounds is that?

4. Ben has a mass of 8 st 10 lb. How many pounds is that?

5. A boxer has a mass of 10 st 7 lb. How many pounds is that?

6. If coal is in 1 cwt bags, how many bags make 2 ton?

7. I had 1 ton of stone. I used 13 cwt for a rockery. How many hundredweight were left?

8. I bought 1 lb of sweets. I ate 2 oz and gave away 8 oz. How many ounces were left?

9. Out of 1 cwt of potatoes, 42 lb were used. How many pounds were left?

10. Liam had an 8 oz box of chocolates and a 4 oz bar of chocolate. How many more ounces did he need to have one pound of chocolate altogether?

Exercise 28

Remember 1 kg = 1000 g

1. Write how many more grams are needed to make 1 kg if you have:
   (a) 800 g   (b) 300 g   (c) 450 g   (d) 760 g

2. A jar of coffee has a total mass of 685 g. If the coffee has a mass of 200 g, what is the mass of the jar?

3. If golf balls each have a mass of 50 g, find the total mass of 4 golf balls.

4. A pack of butter has a mass of 250 g.
   (a) How many packs would you buy in 1 kg?
   (b) How many packs would you buy in 3 kg?

5. A book has a mass of 650 g. Find the total mass of 20 of the books. (Give the answer in kilograms.)

6. A packet of tea has a mass of 125 g.
   (a) Find the total mass of 4 packets.
   (b) Find the total mass of 8 packets.
   (c) How many packets have a total mass of 4 kg?

Exercise 29 Miscellaneous Units of Measure

Copy these, but replace each question mark with $<$, $>$ or $=$ to make each statement correct:

1. Kilometre ⟨ ? ⟩ mile
2. Metre ⟨ ? ⟩ yard
3. Litre ⟨ ? ⟩ pint

4. Tonne ⟨ ? ⟩ ton
5. Kilogram ⟨ ? ⟩ pound
6. Gram ⟨ ? ⟩ ounce

Miscellaneous Information

1. The heaviest recorded man in Great Britain was William Campbell who was born in Glasgow in 1856 and died in 1878. He was 191 cm (6 ft 3 in) tall and had a mass of 340 kg (53 st 8 lb). His waist measured 216 cm (85 in) and his chest 244 cm (96 in). His coffin had a total mass of 680 kg (107 st 2 lb).

2. The largest blue whale ever recorded was 33.58 m long. Another blue whale of length 29.48 m was believed to have a total mass of 177 tonnes (174 tons). A 27.6 m blue whale taken by the Slava whaling fleet in the Antarctic on 17 March 1947 had a tongue that weighed 4.29 tonnes (4.22 tons).

3. The longest animal ever recorded is the ribbon worm. In 1864, one measuring more than 54 m (180 ft) was washed ashore at St. Andrews, Fifeshire, Scotland.

4. The main span of the Humber Estuary Bridge measures 1410 m (4626 ft).

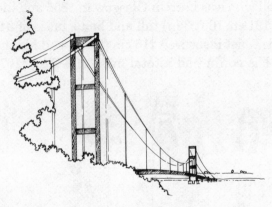

5. In Austria, the Arlberg road tunnel is 14 km (8.7 miles) long.

23 Conversion Graphs and Tables

Copy and complete these scales:

1.   **2.**   **3.**   **4.**   **5.**

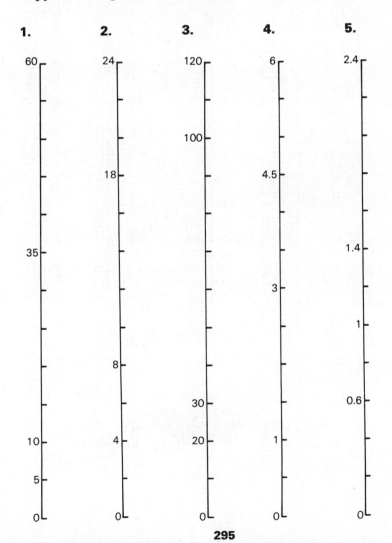

295

Exercise 2

For each question, find the numbers that should be in the places shown by a, b, c, d, e, f, g, h, i, j and k.

1.   2.   3.   4.   5.

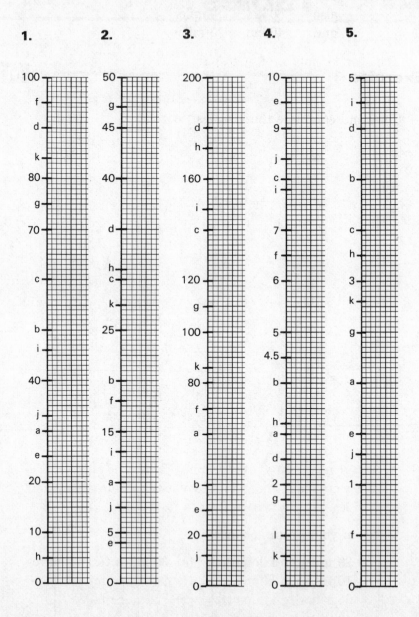

Exercise 3

8 km is about the same distance as 5 miles.

We can write   8 km ≈ 5 miles
      also   80 km ≈ 50 miles
      and   40 km ≈ 25 miles

This can be shown on a graph:

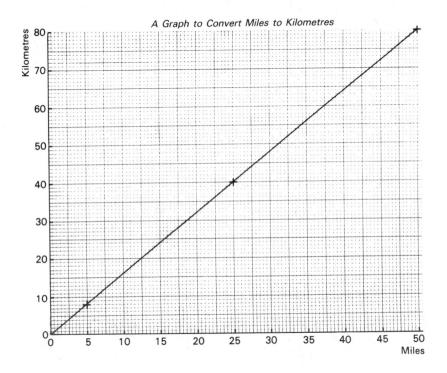

1. Copy the graph above. (Do not forget the title.)
   Use a scale of 2 cm to 5 miles on the horizontal axis and 1 cm to 5 km on the vertical axis.

2. From your graph, change:

   (a) 20 miles to kilometres (e) 30 miles to kilometres
   (b) 10 miles to kilometres (f) 24 km to miles
   (c) 35 miles to kilometres (g) 72 km to miles
   (d) 40 miles to kilometres (h) 60 km to miles

Exercise 4

Draw a graph to convert kilograms to pounds.
Use a scale of 1 cm to 5 kg and 1 cm to 10 lb.

Note: 80 kg = 176 lb
          40 kg =   88 lb
           5 kg =   11 lb

These are shown on the graph below using crosses.

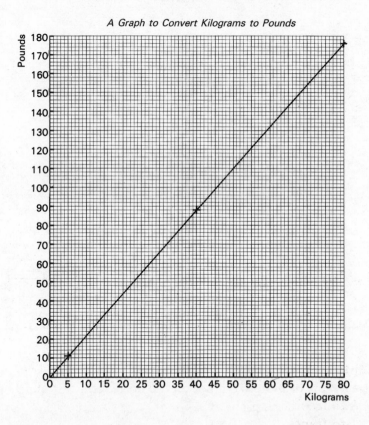

A Graph to Convert Kilograms to Pounds

Use your graph to change:

1. 20 kg to pounds
2. 60 kg to pounds
3. 40 kg to pounds
4. 70 kg to pounds

5. 110 lb to kilograms
6. 66 lb to kilograms
7. 22 lb to kilograms
8. 99 lb to kilograms

Exercise 5

Draw a graph to convert French francs into pounds.
Use a scale of 1 cm to 5 francs and 2 cm to £1.

Use: £8 = 96 francs
and £4 = 48 francs

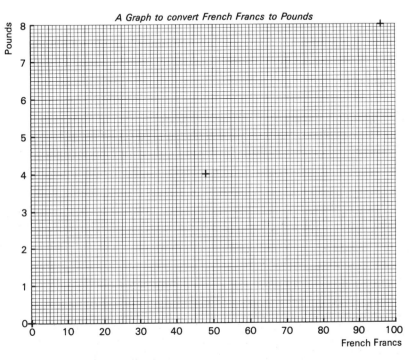

Use your graph to change:

1. 60 francs to pounds
2. 24 francs to pounds
3. 84 francs to pounds
4. £3 to francs
5. £1 to francs
6. £6 to francs
7. £2.50 to francs
8. £6.50 to francs
9. 90 francs to pounds
10. 18 francs to pounds

Conversion Tables

Four conversion tables are given on p. 301.
Look at the first table of length. Look at the row of figures having an 8 in the centre column.

	Centimetres	cm or in	Inches
The row is:	20.32	8	3.15

It shows that: 8 cm = 3.15 in
It also shows that 8 in = 20.32 cm

Exercise 6

Use the tables on p. 301 to convert:

A Centimetres into inches:
   1. 6 cm   **2.** 9 cm   **3.** 20 cm   **4.** 40 cm   **5.** 50 cm

B Inches into centimetres:
   1. 5 in   **2.** 7 in   **3.** 30 in   **4.** 40 in   **5.** 50 in

C Kilometres to miles:
   1. 2 km   **2.** 5 km   **3.** 8 km   **4.** 30 km   **5.** 50 km

D Miles into kilometres:
   1. 3 miles   **2.** 6 miles   **3.** 10 miles   **4.** 20 miles   **5.** 50 miles

E Pounds into kilograms:
   1. 4 lb   **2.** 7 lb   **3.** 9 lb   **4.** 30 lb   **5.** 50 lb

F Kilograms into pounds:
   1. 1 kg   **2.** 3 kg   **3.** 6 kg   **4.** 20 kg   **5.** 50 kg

G Litres to gallons:
   1. 1 *l*   **2.** 3 *l*   **3.** 6 *l*   **4.** 20 *l*   **5.** 50 *l*

H Gallons into litres:
   1. 3 gal   **2.** 6 gal   **3.** 10 gal   **4.** 30 gal   **5.** 50 gal

Conversion Tables

Length

Centimetres	cm or in	Inches
2.54	1	0.39
5.08	2	0.79
7.62	3	1.18
10.16	4	1.58
12.70	5	1.97
15.24	6	2.36
17.78	7	2.76
20.32	8	3.15
22.86	9	3.54
25.40	10	3.94
50.80	20	7.87
76.20	30	11.81
101.60	40	15.75
127.00	50	19.69

Mass

Kilograms	kg or lb	Pounds
0.45	1	2.20
0.91	2	4.41
1.36	3	6.61
1.81	4	8.82
2.27	5	11.02
2.72	6	13.23
3.18	7	15.43
3.63	8	17.64
4.08	9	19.84
4.54	10	22.05
9.07	20	44.09
13.61	30	66.14
18.14	40	88.18
22.68	50	110.2

Length

Kilometres	km or miles	Miles
1.61	1	0.62
3.22	2	1.24
4.83	3	1.86
6.44	4	2.49
8.05	5	3.11
9.66	6	3.73
11.27	7	4.35
12.87	8	4.97
14.48	9	5.59
16.09	10	6.21
32.19	20	12.43
48.28	30	18.64
64.37	40	24.85
80.47	50	31.07

Capacity

Litres	l or gal	Gallons
4.55	1	0.22
9.09	2	0.44
13.64	3	0.66
18.18	4	0.88
22.73	5	1.10
27.28	6	1.32
31.82	7	1.54
36.37	8	1.76
40.91	9	1.98
45.46	10	2.20
90.92	20	4.40
136.4	30	6.60
181.8	40	8.80
227.3	50	11.00

24 Vectors

Exercise 1

Look at the map:

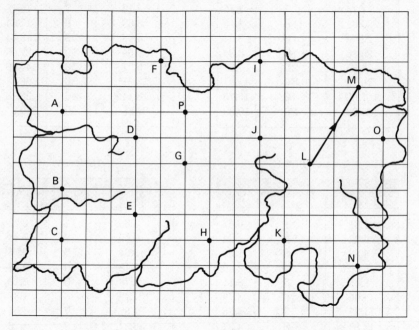

A journey from L to M can be written as $\overrightarrow{LM} = \begin{pmatrix} 2 \\ 3 \end{pmatrix}$.

P to I can be written as $\overrightarrow{PI} = \begin{pmatrix} 3 \\ 2 \end{pmatrix}$.

C to E is $\overrightarrow{CE} = \begin{pmatrix} 3 \\ 1 \end{pmatrix}$ and D to J is $\overrightarrow{DJ} = \begin{pmatrix} 5 \\ 0 \end{pmatrix}$.

E to D is $\overrightarrow{ED} = \begin{pmatrix} 0 \\ 3 \end{pmatrix}$.

Write these journeys in the same way:

1. D to P	**6.** L to O	**11.** H to K
2. A to F	**7.** H to J	**12.** A to P
3. B to D	**8.** C to G	**13.** G to P
4. K to L	**9.** E to F	**14.** B to A
5. E to G	**10.** C to J	**15.** N to M

Exercise 2 M

1. Copy this map on to squared paper:

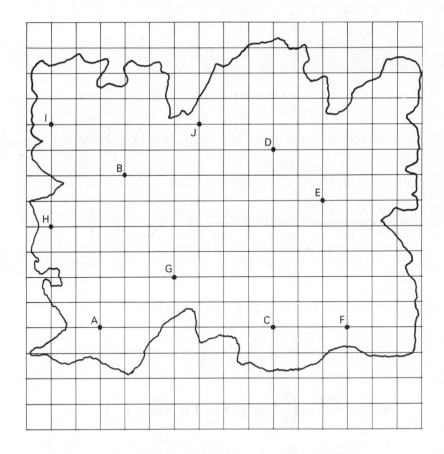

2. Mark all the given places on your copy of the map.

3. Mark on your map the end-point of each of these journeys. (Do not forget to label the points.)

(a) $\overrightarrow{AN} = \begin{pmatrix} 2 \\ 3 \end{pmatrix}$ (e) $\overrightarrow{ER} = \begin{pmatrix} 3 \\ 5 \end{pmatrix}$ (i) $\overrightarrow{IV} = \begin{pmatrix} 4 \\ 2 \end{pmatrix}$

(b) $\overrightarrow{BO} = \begin{pmatrix} 1 \\ 2 \end{pmatrix}$ (f) $\overrightarrow{FS} = \begin{pmatrix} 3 \\ 2 \end{pmatrix}$ (j) $\overrightarrow{JW} = \begin{pmatrix} 3 \\ 3 \end{pmatrix}$

(c) $\overrightarrow{CP} = \begin{pmatrix} 2 \\ 4 \end{pmatrix}$ (g) $\overrightarrow{GT} = \begin{pmatrix} 0 \\ 3 \end{pmatrix}$

(d) $\overrightarrow{DQ} = \begin{pmatrix} 4 \\ 1 \end{pmatrix}$ (h) $\overrightarrow{HU} = \begin{pmatrix} 4 \\ 0 \end{pmatrix}$

Exercise 3

In Exercises 1 and 2 the journeys shown can be called *vectors*.

In this diagram, *all* the arrows show the vector $\begin{pmatrix} 3 \\ 2 \end{pmatrix}$.

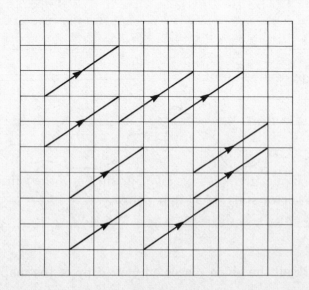

On squared paper, draw three arrows to show each of these vectors:

1. $\begin{pmatrix} 2 \\ 1 \end{pmatrix}$ **3.** $\begin{pmatrix} 2 \\ 3 \end{pmatrix}$ **5.** $\begin{pmatrix} 0 \\ 2 \end{pmatrix}$

2. $\begin{pmatrix} 4 \\ 2 \end{pmatrix}$ **4.** $\begin{pmatrix} 3 \\ 5 \end{pmatrix}$ **6.** $\begin{pmatrix} 3 \\ 0 \end{pmatrix}$

Exercise 4

A Draw a pair of axes. Use a scale of 1 cm to 1 unit on both axes.

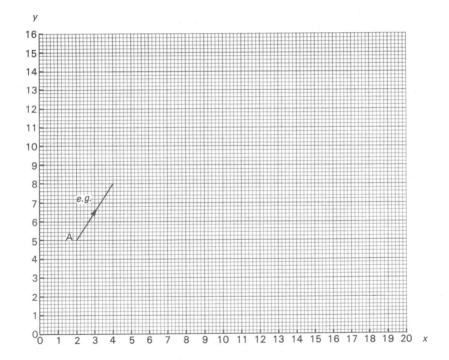

B For each question, plot the given point. Show the journey given by the vector starting at that point.

          Point   Vector

e.g. A = (2, 5) $\begin{pmatrix} 2 \\ 3 \end{pmatrix}$ The answer to this is shown in the diagram above.

	Point	Vector		Point	Vector
1.	B = (4, 2)	$\begin{pmatrix} 3 \\ 2 \end{pmatrix}$	**7.**	H = (6, 7)	$\begin{pmatrix} 7 \\ 4 \end{pmatrix}$
2.	C = (10, 3)	$\begin{pmatrix} 2 \\ 2 \end{pmatrix}$	**8.**	I = (4, 1)	$\begin{pmatrix} 4 \\ 1 \end{pmatrix}$
3.	D = (2, 12)	$\begin{pmatrix} 5 \\ 1 \end{pmatrix}$	**9.**	J = (12, 14)	$\begin{pmatrix} 4 \\ 0 \end{pmatrix}$
4.	E = (16, 1)	$\begin{pmatrix} 1 \\ 6 \end{pmatrix}$	**10.**	K = (19, 10)	$\begin{pmatrix} 0 \\ 5 \end{pmatrix}$
5.	F = (8, 11)	$\begin{pmatrix} 2 \\ 4 \end{pmatrix}$	**11.**	L = (0, 9)	$\begin{pmatrix} 4 \\ 2 \end{pmatrix}$
6.	G = (10, 6)	$\begin{pmatrix} 4 \\ 4 \end{pmatrix}$	**12.**	M = (6, 0)	$\begin{pmatrix} 8 \\ 2 \end{pmatrix}$

Exercise 5

1. A train travels between two stations. Who travels further, someone in the first carriage or someone in the last carriage?

2. A bus is 12 m long. The distance between two bus stops is 400 m. The bus starts when the driver is opposite the first bus then stops when the driver is opposite the second bus stop. How far has:
   (a) the driver travelled?
   (b) a passenger on the back seat travelled?
   (c) a passenger sitting 4 m from the front of the bus travelled?

Revision Exercises XIX to XXIV

Revision Exercise XIX

1. The diameter of a circle is twice the radius. Find the diameter if the radius is 9 cm.

2. The perimeter of a square is four times the length of one of its sides. Find the perimeter of a square with sides:
   (a) 8 cm
   (b) 2.6 m

3.
   $$\text{m} \xrightarrow{\times 100} \text{cm}$$
   Change into centimetres:

   (a) 3 m
   (b) 17 m
   (c) 2.9 m

4. The formula: $A = bh$ gives the area of a parallelogram. Find A when $b = 6$ and $h = 7$.

5. Find the value of:
   (a) $3 \times 6 + 8$
   (b) $12 + 4 \times 5$

6. If $x = 4$, $y = 7$ and $z = 3$ find the value of:
   (a) $x + y$
   (c) $xz + y$
   (b) yz
   (d) $x + z - y$

7. If $u * v$ means $2u + v$, find the value of:
   (a) $3 * 4$
   (b) $5 * 6$
   (c) $12 * 8$

8. Simplify:
   (a) $5d + 2d + 6d$
   (b) $4k + 3m + 6k + 2k + 5m$
   (c) $7p + 2q + p + 3q + 5p$

9. Lucy had $6l$ sweets. She ate $2l$ was given $7l$ and gave $3l$ away.
   (a) How many has she got left?
   (b) How many has she left if $l = 4$?

10. Simplify $3 \times 8d$.

Revision Exercise XX

1. Draw a jagged line graph to show the number of units of electricity used each week for 8 weeks.

Week	1	2	3	4	5	6	7	8
Number of units used	69	72	70	74	81	79	85	93

Use a scale of 2 cm to 1 week and 1 cm to 5 units of electricity.

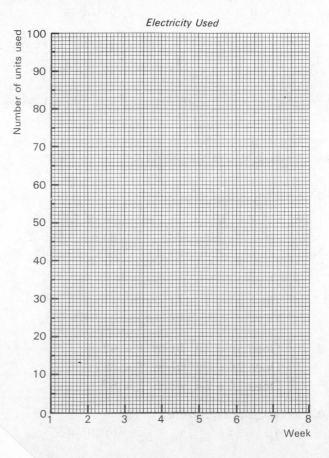

Electricity Used

2. 24 pupils were asked for their favourite subject. Here are the results:

Number of pupils	Number of degrees
24	360
12	
6	
3	
1	
2	
4	
8	

Art 6
English 4
Geography 2
History 4
Maths 8

(a) Copy and complete the table.

(b) Draw a pie chart to show the favourite subjects.

3. Using the digits 3, 5 and 6 once only in each number, make as many different 3-digit numbers as you can.

4. Using two of the digits 2, 3, 6 and 9 at a time, make as many different 2-digit even numbers as you can.

Revision Exercise XXI

1. Solve these equations:
(a) $x + 4 = 10$
(b) $t + 13 = 28$
(c) $m - 7 = 9$
(d) $k - 14 = 27$

2. (a) Does $d + 7 = 16$ when $d = 9$?
(b) Does $n - 9 = 15$ when $n = 6$?
(c) Does $g - 14 = 13$ when $g = 27$?
(d) Does $y + 18 = 26$ when $y = 8$?

3. (a) Does $3f = 18$ when $f = 6$?
(b) Does $2f = 72$ when $f = 36$?
(c) Does $7f = 54$ when $f = 8$?

4. Solve these equations:
(a) $4p = 24$
(b) $3q = 27$

Revision Exercise XXII

Part One

1. Copy and complete these sentences. Use the most suitable metric units:

  (*a*) The bus is 12 ⬚? long

  (*b*) The height of a jam jar is about 125 ⬚?.

  (*c*) An aeroplane is flying at a height of 10 000 ⬚?.

2. The length of a car is about:

  A. 2.4 m   C. 140 cm

  B. 4.3 m   D. 920 mm

3. Estimate the height of a chair seat.

  (*a*) How many metres are there in 600 cm?

  (*b*) How many millimetres are there in 8 m?

  (*c*) How many metres are there in 2 km?

5. Copy and complete:

  (*a*)   5 cm = ⬚? mm   (*g*) 7000 m   = ⬚? km

  (*b*)   80 mm = ⬚? cm   (*h*)   8 km = ⬚? m

  (*c*)   7 m   = ⬚? cm   (*i*)   5.8 km = ⬚? m

  (*d*) 900 cm = ⬚? m   (*j*) 2400 m   = ⬚? km

  (*e*) 4000 mm = ⬚? m   (*k*)   6.7 cm = ⬚? mm

  (*f*)   6 m   = ⬚? mm   (*l*)   82 mm = ⬚? cm

6. Calculate the perimeter of a regular hexagon with sides of 83 mm.

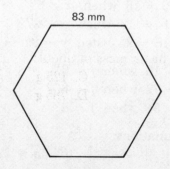

83 mm

7. A square has a perimeter of 32 cm. Find the length of each side.

8. The perimeter of a rectangle is 80 mm. If its length is 24 mm, find its breadth.

9. Draw a straight line PQ, 75 mm long.
Using a protractor, draw angle QPR of 40°.
Draw PR, 55 mm long.
Join QR.
How long is QR?

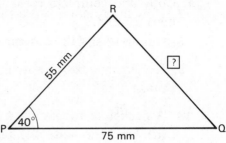

10. (*a*) How many inches are there in 4 ft?
(*b*) Change 6 ft to inches.
(*c*) How many feet are there in 5 yd?
(*d*) Change 12 ft to yards.

Part Two

1. Change 8 *l* to millilitres.

2. Change 7000 m*l* to litres.

3. Change 3 gal to pints.

4. Change 56 pt to gallons.

5. A mug holds about:
A. 250 m*l*   C. 1.5 *l*
B. 150 *l*   D. 95 *l*

6. A carton of milk holds 500 m*l*. How many litres is 6 cartons?

Part Three

1. A packet of tea has a mass of about:
A. 125 mg   C. 125 g
B. 825 mg   D. 785 g

2. Change 6 kg to grams.

3. Change 5000 g to kilograms.

4. Change 3.5 kg to grams.

5. Change 5400 g to kg.

6. How many ounces are there in 3 lb?

7. How many pounds are there in 3 st?

8. Change 6 st 4 lb to pounds.

9. If you have 620 g, how many more grams do you need to make 1 kg?

10. A packet of sweets has a mass of 125 g?
    (*a*) Find the mass of 2 packets.
    (*b*) Find the mass of 5 packets.
    (*c*) How many packets have a total mass of 1 kg?

Revision Exercise XXIII

A Draw a conversion graph to change gallons to litres.

Use a scale of 1 cm to 1 gal and 1 cm to 5 ℓ

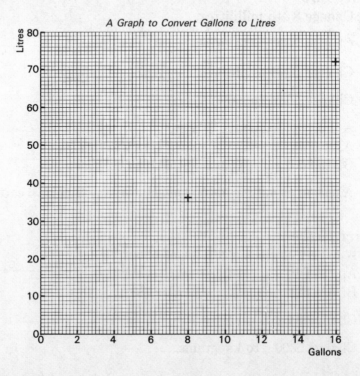

A Graph to Convert Gallons to Litres

Plot the points where 16 gal = 72 ℓ

and 8 gal = 36 ℓ

Use your graph to help you to change:

1. 4 gal into litres
2. 10 gal into litres
3. 6 gal into litres

4. 9 ℓ into gallons
5. 54 ℓ into gallons
6. 63 ℓ into gallons

B Use the conversion table to change:

1. 100 °C into °F
2. 0 °C into °F
3. 40 °C into °F
4. 80 °C into °F
5. 30 °C into °F
6. 50 °C into °F
7. 50 °F into °C
8. 70 °F into °C
9. 60 °F into °C
10. 100 °F into °C
11. 200 °F into °C
12. 0 °F into °C

Temperature

Celsius	°C or °F	°Fahrenheit
⁻23	**⁻10**	14
⁻18	**0**	32
⁻12	**10**	50
⁻ 7	**20**	68
⁻ 1	**30**	86
4	**40**	104
10	**50**	122
16	**60**	140
21	**70**	158
27	**80**	176
32	**90**	194
38	**100**	212
66	**150**	302
93	**200**	392

Revision Exercise XXIV

1. $\overrightarrow{GB}$ is vector $\begin{pmatrix} 1 \\ 2 \end{pmatrix}$

write the vectors

(a) $\overrightarrow{FG}$

(b) $\overrightarrow{EB}$

(c) $\overrightarrow{FH}$

(d) $\overrightarrow{AD}$

(e) $\overrightarrow{AH}$

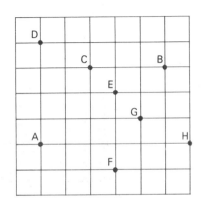

2. (*a*) Which is vector $\begin{pmatrix} 2 \\ 3 \end{pmatrix}$?

(*b*) Which is vector $\begin{pmatrix} 3 \\ 0 \end{pmatrix}$?

3. On squared paper, draw four arrows to show the vector $\begin{pmatrix} 5 \\ 4 \end{pmatrix}$.

4. Draw a pair of axes as in Exercise 4 on p. 305.
Plot the given points. Show each journey given by the vector starting at that point.

	Point	Vector
(*a*)	P = (3, 5)	$\begin{pmatrix} 2 \\ 4 \end{pmatrix}$
(*b*)	Q = (2, 11)	$\begin{pmatrix} 5 \\ 2 \end{pmatrix}$
(*c*)	R = (7, 0)	$\begin{pmatrix} 5 \\ 1 \end{pmatrix}$
(*d*)	S = (10, 8)	$\begin{pmatrix} 7 \\ 0 \end{pmatrix}$
(*e*)	T = (18, 10)	$\begin{pmatrix} 0 \\ 4 \end{pmatrix}$